THE NEW BASIC READERS

CURRICULUM FOUNDATION SERIES

REG. U.S. PAT. OFF.

THE NEW

Friends and Neighbors

The 1956 Edition

William S. Gray, Marion Monroe,
A. Sterl Artley, May Hill Arbuthnot

SCOTT, FORESMAN AND COMPANY

Chicago Atlanta Dallas Palo Alto Fair Lawn, N. J.

Stories

3

Old Friends

The Funny Animal

"Hello, Tom," called Dick.

"Hurry to my house and see something funny."

"What is it?" asked Tom.

"Is it a new toy?"

"I think so," said Dick.

"I think you could call it a toy.

All of you must come and see it."

So Tom and Jim went with Dick.

Patty and Susan went, too.

On the way to Dick's house
the children stopped at Billy's.

"Look at Happy," said Dick.

"What a funny dog he is!

We have a very funny animal
at our house, too!"

"Is it a pet?" asked Billy.

"Can it run and play with you?"

Dick laughed and said, "It can't run.

But I can run and play with it.

You and Nancy must come and see it."

Soon Dick saw Peter and Ellen.

"Come and see the big new animal
in our yard," Dick said.

"How big is it?" asked Peter.

"Is it as big as a cow or a horse?"

Dick laughed and said, "Not that big!

It is flying over our back yard."

"Oh, my!" said Ellen.

"Then it can't be a cow or a horse.

It must be a big, big bird.

Let's hurry and see it!"

8

"There it is," said Dick.

"There is our big flying pig."

All Dick's friends laughed
at the funny big pig.

"Oh, Dick," Jim said at last.

"It is just what you said it was.

You can call it a toy.

It is big, and it is funny.

It is an animal, and it can fly.

But how could we guess that it
was anything like this?"

What Will You Buy?

Jane and Spot were going up the street
as fast as they could.

So were Jack and Jim.

"Get out of the way," called the boys.

But just then Jane stopped.

The boys stopped, too.

"Look, boys!" said Jane.

"See what I have in my pocket."

"Pennies!" said Jack.

"What are you going to buy with them?
Is it a toy for Spot?"

"Oh, no!" laughed Jane.

"It is something round and red."

"An apple?" guessed the boys.

"No!" said Jane.

"I'll let you see it when I come back
from the store!"

Then Jane and Spot went hurrying on.

11

"Stop, Jane, stop," called two girls.

"Where are you going?"

"To Mrs. Hill's store," said Jane.

"See what I have in my pocket."

"Pennies!" said Ellen and Susan.

"What will you buy with them?"

"Something round and red," said Jane.

"Is it a new ball?" asked Ellen.

"Not a ball," laughed Jane.

"I'll let you see it when I come back."

At Mrs. Hill's store Jane met
the milkman.

"Look, Mr. Wills!" Jane said.

"See what I have in my pocket."

"Oh, pennies!" said the milkman.

"What will you buy with them?"

"Something pretty," said Jane.

"It is round and red.

Guess what it is."

Mr. Wills began to think.

He thought and thought.

At last Mr. Wills said, "I can't
guess what it is."

"Oh, yes! Yes, you can," Jane said.

"Think of a name that has a J in it."

"Oh, I know," said the milkman.

"Could it be a jumping jack?"

"Not that," laughed Jane.

"But you may see what I get when I
come out of the store."

Soon Jane came running out.

There on the walk was the milkman.

There were Susan, Ellen, Jack, and Jim.

"Look," Jane called to her friends.

"My!" said Jim and Jack.

"How pretty!" said Ellen and Susan.

"We did not think of that."

"Well, well, Jane," said the milkman.

"Now I know why you laughed
at my guess.

You said the name had a J in it.

But I did not think of your name.

I did not think of JANE."

Over I Go

"Hurry, Jim," called Jack.

"Jump faster!

Here I come behind you."

Jump, jump, jump went Jim.

Over Billy.

Over Patty.

Over Dick.

"Over I go," called Jack.

Then he began to jump.

Over Peter.

Over Susan.

Over Billy.

Over Patty.

Over Dick.

But when Jack came to Jim,
he had to stop.

"Down, Jim, down," he called.

"Put your head down."

"Like this?" asked Jim.

"Not like that," laughed Jack.

"Get down so I can jump over you."

Then Jack went back behind Peter
and began to jump again.

Over the children he went.

One, two, three, four, five.

When he came to Jim, he stopped.

"Oh, Jim!" he said, "Get down!

Put your head way, way down."

"Like this?" asked Jim.

"Is this the way to do it?"

"No, Jim, no!" laughed Jack.

"Don't be so funny!

I'll have to push you down."

Jack pushed down on Jim and said,

"Over I go."

But Jack did not go over.

It was Jim who went over.

He went over so fast that everyone
was surprised.

"Oh, Jim," laughed Jack.

"What a funny boy you are!

When your head is up,
your feet are down.

When your head is down,
your feet go up.

No one can jump over you."

Here Comes Father

It was time for Billy's father
to come home from work.

It was raining, and Billy was going
to the streetcar with an umbrella.

Splash, splash went Billy's two feet
on the walk.

Splash, splash, splash, splash went
Happy's four feet as he ran after Billy.

Billy and Happy came to the car stop
just as the streetcar did.

The door opened, and a woman came out.

Next a big boy came out.

Next came two girls.

Then a man came out.

Was that Father?

No, it was the man who lived next door.

Bang! went the streetcar door, and
the car went on.

"Father will come on the next car,"
Billy said to Happy.

Soon another car came along, but it was going to town.

Father could not be on that car.

The next car came from town, but Billy could not see who came out.

All he could see were umbrellas.

Big ones and little ones!

Black ones and red ones!

Blue, green, and yellow!

Splash, splash came the rain.

Faster and faster and faster!

Billy looked down at the feet
that came from the car.

"I'll know Father's feet when I
see them," he thought.

Splash, splash, splash, splash!
The feet came along very fast.
Big feet and little feet!
Black, red, white, and brown!
Billy looked and looked.
But he did not see any feet
that looked like Father's.

"Oh, dear," thought Billy.

"Father did not come on that car."

All at once Happy ran out and said,
"Bow-wow, bow-wow!"

Two big feet came to a stop, and
Billy looked up.

He said, "Oh, Father! I did not know
which feet were yours.

But Happy did."

Then down the walk splashed big feet
and little feet.

Two feet were Father's.

Two were Billy's, and four of them
were Happy's.

I Think I Will

One day Tom was buying something at Mrs. Hill's store.

"Here are all my pennies," he said.

Then he walked out with something that was very good to eat.

He had three big round cookies.

One cookie was white.

One cookie was brown, and one had nuts all over it.

"I'll eat one now," thought Tom.

But just then he met Dick.

"Look, Dick," said Tom.

"See what I have in here."

"Three big cookies!" said Dick as he peeped in at them.

"Cookies from Mrs. Hill's store! They look very good!"

"Have one," said Tom.

"Thank you, I think I will," Dick said.

He took the brown cookie and walked away eating it.

Soon Tom saw a woman working
in her yard.

"Good morning, Mrs. Black," he called.

"See what I have."

"Oh!" said Mrs. Black.

"What fine big cookies!"

"Have one!" said Tom.

"Thank you, I think I will,"
said Mrs. Black.

She took the white cookie and
began to eat it.

At the next street Tom met
another one of his friends.

"Look, Big Bill!" Tom said.

"Have a cookie!"

"I think I will," said Big Bill.

"I am too busy to go home and
eat my dinner."

Big Bill took the cookie that had
nuts all over it.

"Thank you," he said as he began
to stop some cars.

"Now I'll have a cookie," said Tom.

But there was no cookie for him.

When he came home, his mother said,
"Hello, Tom.

See what I made for dinner."

"Oh! Cookies!" said Tom.

"Yes, have one," said his mother.

"Thank you, I think I will," said Tom.

He took a big brown cookie and
began to eat it.

"M-m-m!" he said.

"This is as good as any cookie
in Mrs. Hill's store."

New Friends
and Neighbors

Here, There, Anywhere

The Flying Jack Rabbit
was running on Pleasant Street.

"Where is the train going?"
Jane asked when it stopped.

"To any town you like," said Dick.

"Here, there, anywhere!"

"I'll ride to the next town," Jane said.

Jim helped her into the first car.

Then the train went on its way.

Soon the train slowed down.

Jim called, "Green Town! All out."

Jane got out, but two of her neighbors
were there to get in.

Jim helped Tom and Susan in.

Then the Flying Jack Rabbit went on.

Next Jim called, "New Town!"

No one got out, but Ellen got in.

Up and down Pleasant Street went
the train.

It stopped here. It stopped there.

Children got in. Children got out.

At Hill Road, Tom and Susan got out.

Then other children got out.

One here. One there.

Soon there was no one but Ellen
in the Flying Jack Rabbit.

The train slowed down again, and
Jim called, "Toy Town, Toy Town!"

Ellen was not going there.

So she did not get out.

The next stop was Five Trees, but
Ellen was not going there.

On and on went the train.

The boys called town after town.

But Ellen did not get out.

At last Dick stopped the train and looked back at her.

"Where are you going?" he asked.

"Home!" said Ellen.

Jim said, "Why, Ellen! We stopped at your house four or five times.

Why didn't you get out there?"

"You didn't call **Home**," said Ellen.

"You didn't call it once."

Dick backed the train down the hill
to Ellen's house.

"Home! Home!" he called, and
Ellen got out.

"Thank you," she said.

"That was a very fine ride."

Dick and Jim did not say anything.

Jim sat down in his wagon.

Dick sat down, too.

They sat and sat and sat.

They did not play train again very soon.

Not for days and days and days!

Mrs. Hill's Birthday

Mrs. Hill lived in a little white house on Pleasant Street.

One room of the house was her store.

In the store were all the things that the neighbor children liked.

There were things to eat and things to play with.

Candy, cookies, apples, and nuts! Storybooks and toys!

One morning Mrs. Hill had to make cookies and candy for her store.

All at once the bell over her door began to buzz.

Mrs. Hill thought someone had come in. So she peeped into the store.

"Dear me!" she said in surprise.

"The door opened, but no one came in.

Maybe the wind pushed the door open and made my bell buzz."

Soon the bell began to buzz again.
This time Mrs. Hill saw
Jack and Dick walk in.

She went into the store to get
candy apples for them.

She did not see the basket at the door.
But the boys saw it.

They looked at it and asked,
"What day is it, Mrs. Hill?"

"It is Saturday," she said.

"On Saturday you children buy candy
and cookies as fast as I make them."

All morning Mrs. Hill's doorbell
buzzed and buzzed.

All morning children came to buy candy
or nuts or toys or storybooks.

Every one of them looked at the basket.

Every one of them laughed and asked,
"What day is it, Mrs. Hill?"

To all of them she said, "Saturday!
Saturday is my busy day."

All at once she heard, "Bow-wow."

She said, "I think I heard a dog."

But just then the doorbell buzzed, and
in came Susan.

"What day is it?" asked Susan.

"It is Saturday!" said Mrs. Hill.

"Why do all of you ask me that?"

"Don't you know why?" Susan asked.

Mrs. Hill began to think.

"Well, well," she said at last.

"This is my birthday! I was so busy
that I didn't think of it."

Just then Mrs. Hill heard
another "Bow-wow."

Then she saw the basket.

She began to read what was on it.

Happy Birthday, Mrs. Hill

From your friends

and neighbors

on Pleasant Street.

Other neighbor children
came and peeped in.

They saw Mrs. Hill open
the basket.

They heard her say, "Oh, oh!

Here is a puppy!

A fat little, brown little puppy!

All of you came in to see me find
the basket.

All morning you made my doorbell
go buzz, buzz, buzz.

So I think I will name
the puppy Buzz."

A New Game

"Oh, Jill! Oh, Ann!" called a boy.

"Come and play with us."

Jill and Ann looked up the street
and down the street.

No one was there.

"I know I heard a boy call us,"
said Ann.

"I think it was Billy."

"Let's see if he is in the yard,"
said Jill.

But there was no one in the yard.

No one on the walk.

No one at all on Pleasant Street.

Ann said, "Come and play, Jill.
Let's play with my dolls."

The girls ran into the house. But they
did not play with the dolls.

The dolls were not in Ann's room.

Ann did not see them anywhere.

All at once the girls saw a letter
on the dollhouse.

Ann opened the letter, and the girls began to read it.

The letter said,

Dear Jill and Ann,
Look for the dolls in the
Billy   Tom   Dick

"What a funny letter!" laughed Jill.

"I think the boys took the dolls away to play a new game.

They want us to play the game, too.

They want us to read this letter and guess where the dolls are."

Ann looked at the letter again.

Then she said, "Now I can guess where the dolls are.

The letter tells where to find them.

Come outdoors with me, Jill."

The dolls were not where Ann thought
they were. But a letter was there.

"Just another letter!" Jill said.

"Let's read it and see if it tells
where the dolls are."

The letter said,

Run to the

Billy   Tom   Dick

Ann said, "Come, Jill. I know where
to look next."

Away she ran, with Jill behind her.

"Another letter!" said Ann.

"It may tell us where to find the dolls."

Then she began to read.

Look under the big 🌳

🚶 Billy   🏃 Tom   🧍 Dick

"Oh! The boys didn't put
the dolls here," Ann said.

"This letter tells us to look
under the big tree next."

Jill said, "I think this game is fun.

Let's run to the tree and see
if the dolls are there."

Away they ran to the back yard.

There under the tree sat
the lost dolls.

Behind the tree were three boys.

One of them called, "Hello, girls, hello!
Did you like our new game?"

"Not at first," laughed Jill.

"Ann didn't like it at all when she
thought her dolls were lost.

But finding them with letters was
a funny guessing game for Ann and me."

"It was fun for us, too," said the boys.

How Joe Helped

The children on Pleasant Street were going to Patty's birthday party.

Some of them had stopped at the store to buy things for Patty.

Joe looked and looked. But he could not find what he wanted.

He looked all over the store.

He went from one side to the other.

He looked at games on one side.

He looked at toys on the other side.

"Hurry, Joe, and find something
for Patty," said the other children.

Then they began to tell Joe what to buy.

Billy said, "Patty likes storybooks.
Buy a storybook for her."

"I guess I will," Joe said.

"Here is a good storybook. It is
the story of a lost dog.

Now we can go to the birthday party."

When the children looked outside,
they saw that it was raining.

"Oh, my! We can't go out!" said Ann.

"Maybe Mrs. Hill can help us.
Maybe she has an umbrella."

Just then Patty's Uncle Peter
came running into the store.

"Hello!" he called to the children.

"It is time to go to the party."

Joe said, "We know it is. But we
can't go outside in the rain."

"I wish we had umbrellas," said Jill.

"So do I," said Uncle Peter.

"I must take balloons to the party.
But I don't want to go out
in the rain again."

51

Mrs. Hill said, "I could help you if I could find my old umbrella.

I wish I could think where it is.

Maybe I let someone have it, or maybe I lost it."

"My, my!" said Uncle Peter.

"Rain or no rain, I'll have to take the balloons to Patty."

When Mrs. Hill took the balloons down, something fell with a bump and a bang.

"My lost umbrella!" she said.

"Good!" said Uncle Peter.

"Now we can all go to the party."

"All of us can't go under one umbrella,"
Joe said.

"We can if I take two at a time,"
said Uncle Peter.

First he took the two girls.

Then he went back with the umbrella
and got Jack and Billy.

Last of all he took Joe and Tom.

Patty met them at the door.

She said, "Oh, I am glad you are here.
Did you get the balloons, Uncle Peter?"

"Yes, I did," said Patty's uncle.

But when he looked, he said, "Oh, my!
I lost the balloons."

Joe said, "The balloons are not lost.
You didn't take them out of the store."

"Well, well," said Uncle Peter.

"I went to the store three times,
but I didn't get what I went for.

I was too busy trying to get all of you
to Patty's birthday party.

Now I'll go back for the balloons."

Then Joe laughed and said, "Oh, no!

I took all the balloons when you
went out with Jack and Billy.

See how big we can make them!"

New Friends

John Hill was going away.

He was going to ride on a train
for the very first time.

He was going to the city to see
Grandmother Hill.

Too-oo! went the train as it came in.

Sh-sh! it went as it slowed down.

Then it stopped, and John got on.

"Good-by, good-by!" he called.

"Good-by, John," said his family.

"Don't get lost in the city."

Too-oo! Away went the train.

Faster and faster and faster!

On and on and on!

The train stopped at little towns, and it stopped at big towns.

But John did not get out.

He was going on to the city.

On and on went the train, and at last it came to the city.

When the train stopped, John was the first one to get out.

Then he saw his grandmother.

John's grandmother took him away
in her car.

Up one street and down another
they went.

At last they came to Pleasant Street
and stopped at Mrs. Hill's house.

John jumped out and looked all around.

Then he said, "Oh, Grandmother!
I don't think I'll like the city.

I don't see any children to play
with me."

Just then John saw a balloon go flying
into the yard next door.

"Oh, look!" he said.

"A balloon got away from someone!
It looks like a funny fat pig."

John ran into the yard to see if he
could get the balloon.

But a little puff of wind took it up
over his head.

Bang! went the balloon into a tree.
Then some children ran into the yard.
One boy said, "Hello! My name is Joe.
We saw you try to get Dick's balloon,
and we know who you are.
We heard your grandmother say
that you were going to be here.
We are very glad you came."
Now John was glad to be in the city.
It was going to be fun to play
with new friends on Pleasant Street.

A Funny Telephone

One day John went to see Joe.

As John looked all around, he said,
"What a big house!

What do you do with so many rooms?"

"We don't live in all of them," said Joe.
"Our family lives in just four rooms.

There are many, many homes here, and
we have many, many neighbors."

Just then the boys heard a door bang.

"There is Jack," said Joe.

"Look at him! He is going to talk
to me on our telephone line."

Then John saw a line that ran
from Jack's back door to Joe's.

He saw Jack tie something white
on the line.

"Here comes a letter," Joe said as
Jack began to pull on the line.

But the letter fell, and Jack
had to tie it on the line again.

Then he began to pull on his side
of the line. ·

This time the letter came all the way
to Joe.

Joe began to tell his new friend
how the telephone worked.

"We play we are talking when we
tie letters on the line," said Joe.

John said, "Oh, my! What will I
see next in the city?

At the farm we put clothes
on our clothesline.

We don't use it for a telephone."

"Mother uses this line for clothes, too,"
laughed Joe.

"But if there are no clothes on it,
Jack and I tie letters on it.

Let's see what this letter says."

The letter looked like this.

I am going to play ⊘
at Jim's 🏠 .
🏃 down and play with us.
                Jack

John laughed at the funny letter.

Then Joe asked, "Do you want to do what Jack tells us to do?"

"Oh, yes! Let's go to Jim's house," said John.

"I want to see how you play ball.

Boys who tie letters on clotheslines may have a funny way to play ball."

"Maybe we do," laughed Joe.

"Let's hurry down and go with Jack. Then you will see how we play."

"I am glad you could read my letter,"
Jack said when the three boys met.

John said, "It was a very funny letter.
You use clotheslines in funny ways, too.

Now I want to see how you play ball."

Jack laughed and said, "Joe and I
use a clothesline for a telephone.

But we know just one way
to play ball."

Soon John found out that city boys
play ball just the way farm boys do.

John Uses His Head

"Look! See all my money," said Jim.
"My pockets are full of pennies."
Then he pulled some out
for John to see.

"Where did you get so many pennies?"
asked John in surprise.

"From my father and my Uncle Peter,"
said Jim.

"This is my birthday, and I can use
my money for anything I please.

My father and my uncle said I could."

"Pockets full of money!" John said.

"What will you do with all of it?"

"Oh, I think I'll use it to go
to the park," said Jim.

"You and I can have fun there.

We will ride on a pony.

We will ride on a little blue train.

We will ride around and around
on a merry-go-round."

John looked surprised.

He said, "Why, Jim! There is no pony
in the park on Pleasant Street.

There is no merry-go-round or train."

"Oh!" said Jim. "I will not take you
to the Pleasant Street park.

We are going to the big park. It is
on the other side of the city.

We must ride there on the streetcar."

A car came along, and the boys got on.

Then Jim pulled out some money.

Ten pennies for his ride, and ten
for John's ride.

The car went on and on and on.

Jim wanted the car to go faster, but
John wanted it to go slower.

He thought the streetcar ride was fun.

He wished that his pockets were full
of money so he could ride all day.

At last the car came to the park, and
the boys got out.

In the park there was a merry-go-round
with horses of many colors.

John and Jim went around and around
on the merry-go-round.

They had a ride on a little blue train
and went all around the park.

They had a ride on a fat brown pony
and went galloping, galloping, galloping.

Jim had to pay for every ride.

Soon a man came along with balloons.
Yellow, green, blue, and all colors!
"Let's take two balloons," said Jim.
"Tell me which color you like, John.
My pockets are full of money.
I can buy everything we want."
Jim had to pay the man ten pennies
for the two balloons.

Next the boys got candy and nuts.
Jim had to pay for them, too.
Five pennies to pay for the candy.
Five pennies to pay for the nuts.

At last it was time to go home.

"Now we will ride on the streetcar,"
John said.

"We will have another good ride."

"I'll get the money," said Jim as he
pulled things out of his pockets.

He found ten pennies in one pocket
and no money at all in the other.

"Ten pennies are all I have,"
Jim said.

"I can't pay for two rides
with just ten pennies.

If we want to get home, we must walk."

So the boys began to walk.

They walked and walked and walked.

"Oh, my feet, my feet!" said Jim.

"How I wish my pockets were full
of money now! Then we could ride."

All at once John said, "Look, Jim! There is a telephone in this store.

You can call your family."

Jim laughed and said, "Oh, yes! My ten pennies will pay for the call.

I'll ask Uncle Peter to come in the car and take us home.

Why didn't I use my head and think of the telephone at first?"

John said, "I didn't want to use my feet to walk all the way home.

So I just had to use my head."

71

The Good-by Party

Up Mrs. Hill's walk came the children
on Pleasant Street.

"Surprise, surprise!" they called.

John and Buzz ran to the door.

"Look, Grandmother!" John said.

"Here come all my friends."

"Yes, John," said Mrs. Hill.

"You are going home in the morning.
So your friends will say good-by today.

This is a good-by party for you."

The children began to play
Drop the Handkerchief.

Jill got Jim's handkerchief and
began to run around with it.

Soon she let it drop behind Sally.

Buzz saw the handkerchief drop first
and ran away with it.

Then Sally used Dick's handkerchief
and let it drop behind Jane.

But Buzz ran back and got it, too.

"We can't play this game," said John.

"Buzz will get the handkerchief
every time we drop it."

"Let's play a new game," said Billy.

"I'll tie my handkerchief over my eyes.

Then someone will call like an animal,
and I'll try to guess who it is."

After Billy had tied the handkerchief
over his eyes, Jane called, "Bow-wow."

"That was Susan!" said Billy.

"No, no, guess again," said Susan.

Just then Billy heard, "Mew, mew."

This time he thought it was Peter.

But it was not Peter or any
of the others.

"You can't guess," laughed Sally.

"Pull the handkerchief away, Billy.

Pull it away from your eyes."

Billy pulled the handkerchief away
from his eyes and looked down.

There sat Sally's yellow cat.

Puff was looking at Billy and saying,
"Mew, mew! Mew, mew!"

The children laughed and laughed
at Billy's surprise.

John said, "Our pets are funny today.
They want to play all our games, too."

Just then Mrs. Hill called the children.

"Come in! I have something good
for the party," she said.

The children went in to eat. They had
cookies and candy and apples and milk.

Buzz and Puff had milk, too.

At last the good-by party was over.

The children all said, "Good-by, John.

We wish you could stay here
on Pleasant Street all the time."

"Thank you," said John.

"I have had fun here in the city, but
I must go home to Hill Farm.

I want to see my family.

If you come to our farm sometime,
we can all have fun there, too."

Animal
Friends

Long-Tail

One day Dick heard a funny noise
in Sally's playhouse.

He thought it was Puff mewing. So he
opened the door to see.

What a surprise Dick had!

There was Sally's big yellow cat
with three baby kittens around her.

"Oh, my!" said Dick. "I must tell
Sally and Jane."

As soon as the two girls heard about the kittens, they ran to see them.

But on the way Sally stopped to look at something gray under a tree.

"It looks like a funny baby kitten," she said.

"Its eyes are not open," said Dick.

"How did this kitten get here?"

Dick took the baby to Puff.

"Here is another kitten, Puff," he said. "Didn't you know that it was lost?"

"Mew, mew," said the cat as she looked up at Dick.

At dinner the three children talked
about nothing but Puff's kittens.

"Three are yellow, and one is gray,"
said Sally.

"The gray one got lost," said Jane.
"But Sally found it under a tree today.

It has a very long tail. So we
named it Long-Tail."

Mother looked surprised.

"Is Long-Tail bigger than the others?"
she asked.

"No," said Dick. "He is not bigger.

But his tail is bigger. It is as long
as he is."

"Well, well," said Father. "I must see
the kitten with a tail as big as that.

Mother and I must go out and
see him after dinner."

Mother and Father both laughed
when they saw Long-Tail.

"He is not a kitten," said Father.

"He is a baby squirrel!

He fell from his nest in the tree,
and his mother did not find him.

But he may stay with Puff because
she thinks he is a kitten."

Then Dick thought of something funny.

"Oh, my," he laughed.

"What will Puff think when Long-Tail
wants to live in a tree?

Will Puff think he is a kitten then?"

A Duck and His Quack

Jack and Joe had a pet duck that was
named J. J.

J for Jack, and J for Joe.

The duck stayed first at Joe's house
and then at Jack's.

But both boys played with the pet.

One day Jack said, "Our duck is
getting bigger, and soon he will quack.

Then we will have to do something
with him because of his noise.

The people who live here don't like
a pet that makes noise."

J. J.'s first quack was a little one.

Soon he was quacking more and more.

Every quack was getting bigger, and
the neighbors were talking about him.

They said, "That duck is getting too big.

He is getting so big that he makes
more noise than the children.

He is getting too big to stay here."

The two boys heard the people talking.

Then Joe said, "J. J. must forget
about quacking."

"He can't forget," said Jack.

"A duck can't forget how to quack."

"Maybe we can hide J. J.," said Joe. "Then people will forget about him."

"Yes, we can hide him," laughed Jack.

"But that will not help, because we can't ever hide his quacks.

We will have to give our duck away."

The boys took J. J. up the street.

At every house that had a back yard, they asked, "Do you want a duck today?"

People took one look at J. J. and said, "No, not today!

We have more pets now than we know what to do with."

So the boys took the duck back home.

"We will have to forget about finding a home for our pet!" said Joe.

"And people will have to forget about the noise J. J. makes."

One day when J. J. went down
in the yard, he had a surprise.

Mrs. Hill's dog, Buzz, was there.

The duck quacked and began to run.

"Bow-wow!" said Buzz.

There was more noise than ever
as the dog ran after the duck.

All the neighbors looked out, and
so did Jack and Joe.

Just then J. J. and Buzz ran out
to the street.

Jack and Joe ran down after them.

But when the boys got to the street,
the dog and duck were not there.

The boys thought J. J. was lost forever.
But just then they heard the puppy.

He was in the park, and both boys
ran over to him.

Then they heard a big quacking noise.

"Look! There is J. J.!" said Jack.

"All the ducks in the park
are quacking at him."

"Well!" laughed Joe. "We didn't know
where to find a home for our pet.

But Buzz did!

Buzz found a home in the park
for J. J. and his quack."

Pet Can Do It Better

Old Pet sat on her nest in the barn
at Hill Farm.

John and Nancy Ann saw her there
when they went to the barn with Father.

"You funny hen!" Nancy Ann said.

"Why don't you stay with the hens
in the chicken yard?"

John was about to take Pet off her nest
when he saw some eggs under her.

"Look," he said. "Pet has ten eggs
in her nest. I'll take them to the house."

"No, no!" Mr. Hill said. "Pet hides her eggs because she wants a family.

If she stays on her nest long enough, baby chickens will come out of her eggs."

"Will she get off the nest long enough to eat and get some water?" asked John.

"See if you can find out," said Father.

Both John and Nancy Ann ran out to the barn four or five times a day.

But every time Pet was on her eggs.

At last John got some corn and took it to Pet. He got some water for her, too.

Then the two children sat down.

They wanted to see if Pet ever got off her nest to eat.

They sat and sat and sat.
So did Pet.

After dinner John and his father heard
a big noise at the barn.

Cluck, cluck! Oh, oh, oh!

"That is Pet!" shouted John.

"And your sister!" shouted his father.

They both ran to the barn as fast
as they could.

Mrs. Hill heard the noise. So she
ran to the barn, too.

They were all just in time to see
the hen flying at Nancy Ann.

"Oh, oh!" said Nancy Ann.

"Pet came flying at me just because I wanted to help her.

I thought she could get off her nest and eat if I sat on her eggs."

"Oh, Nancy Ann!" laughed Mrs. Hill.

"Pet knows that she can do it better than you can.

If you sat on Pet's eggs, she could not have any little chickens."

Next day John and his sister saw that Pet's water and food were gone.

They took some to her again, but the next day that was gone, too.

Every day the children took food and water to the hen.

But not once did they see her get off her nest and eat.

One day the children had a surprise.

When they took food and water
to the barn, they met Pet.

Behind her was a long line
of baby chickens.

"Oh!" said John. "Pet could hide
her eggs, but she can't hide her chickens."

Just then it began to rain.

"Get the chickens!" said Nancy Ann.
"Help me get them out of the rain."

"No, no," John said to his sister.

"Don't try to be a mother
to the baby chickens.

Look at old Pet!

She can do it better."

Billy Calf Runs Away

Billy Calf lived at Hill Farm.

He was big enough to eat grass, but he did not like the grass in the barnyard.

The grass outside looked better to him. So he wanted to get out and eat it.

He was about to get out one day when John and his sister saw him.

"Don't, Billy! Don't go out," said John.

"If you ever go there, you will wish you had stayed inside."

One day the Hill family went to town.

After they had gone, Billy bumped
and pushed on the barnyard fence.

All at once he made a big hole in it.

The hole was big enough for Billy Calf
to get out.   So out he jumped.

Then he began to eat the green grass
along the side of the road.

How good that grass was!

Billy walked, and he ate.   Then he
walked and ate some more.

He ate first on one side of the road
and then on the other side.

At last Billy Calf came to a yard.

It was full of fine green grass, but
it had a high fence all around it.

A sign was painted on the fence.

The sign said "Look out for the dog."
But Billy could not read the sign.

He put his head over the fence to look
at the grass on the other side.

Just then a big brown dog ran out and
jumped at Billy's head.

Billy ran off as fast as he could.

"M-a-a! M-a-a!" he said.

Soon Billy came to the big, big road.

A yellow sign said "Stop."

But the calf could not read the sign,
and he did not stop.

Lines of cars were going and coming
on both sides of Billy.

Some cars stopped and began to honk.

The people in them began to shout.

Honk, honk! Honk, honk! went the cars.

"Get off the road," shouted the people.

Billy Calf did not know which way
to go. So a man got out to help him.

The man took the calf off the road, and
the honking cars went on.

Soon Billy Calf came to a white sign.

The sign was high over the road
for everyone to read.

But Billy could not read. So he
did not know that the sign said "Stop."

Then the calf heard a big noise.

A train was coming, but Billy jumped
to one side just in time.

The calf began running down the road.

He ran for a long, long time. Then he
slowed down and began to walk.

Slower and slower and slower he went.

At last the calf came to a white fence.
It had a hole in it and a sign over it.

Billy could not read the sign, but he
saw the hole.

It was the hole he had made.

Then he heard John shout, "Oh, Billy!
We thought you had gone for good.

Where did you go?"

Billy could not talk, and he did not tell.

After that the grass in the barnyard
looked better to Billy.

The grass at home was good enough
for him.

Black Tim

John and his sister had many pets
on the farm.

At feeding time the pets all went
to the house as fast as they could.

But Black Tim got his food first
because he could see it first.

Every morning the crow sat high up
in a tree in the back yard.

"Caw! Caw! Caw!" he called when he
saw the children coming out with food.

Then down he went to get it.

When John and Nancy Ann played
a game in the yard, Tim played, too.

He flew high overhead and called,
"Caw, caw, caw!"

Sometimes the children wanted to hide
from the crow.

But Tim's little round eyes
could see them anywhere.

One day Tim began to play tricks.

First he pulled the dog's tail and
flew off with some of its food.

When John made him stop that trick,
the crow began to play other tricks.

He pulled the kittens' tails and
splashed milk all over them.

When John heard the kittens mewing,
he ran out and made Tim fly away.

But the crow did not go far.

He flew to the clothesline and walked
along on the clothes.

Mrs. Hill was coming with more clothes.
She began to shout at the bird.

"Go away, Tim," she shouted.

"This is a new kind of trick, but it
is not a funny one."

"Caw, caw, caw," said Tim as he
flew up into the tree.

Soon Mrs. Hill went back to the house.

She was busy getting dinner when she
heard the children calling her.

"Look out here, Mother!
Look out at the clothesline."

Then Mother looked outdoors.

"Oh, dear me!" she said in surprise.
"Some of the clothes are gone."

But when she ran out to the yard,
she had a bigger surprise.

Tim was playing another kind of trick.

He was pulling clothes off the line
as fast as he could.

"Stop, Tim, stop!" shouted Mrs. Hill.
"Don't drop any more clothes."

Off flew the crow, and soon he
was far, far away.

John and Nancy Ann helped Mother
put the clothes on the line.

"Please make that crow stay away
from the clothes," said Mother.

"If he comes back here, put him
under a basket."

Both children laughed and said,
"We will have to catch him first."

Then far away they heard Tim's "Caw."

"Now Tim is laughing," said John.
"What a funny bird he is!"

"He is getting too funny," said Mother.

"Who knows what kind of trick
he will play next?"

Finding a Pet

Honey, Bunny, and Funny were sisters.

They lived next to Hill Farm.

They had other names, but everyone called them Honey, Bunny, and Funny.

Funny had a pony to ride.

Bunny had a pet goat that pulled her around in a little green wagon.

Honey did not have a pony or a goat.

She did not want a big pet.

She wanted a little pet to play with.

One day Honey said to her father,
"A pony and a goat are too big for me."
Father laughed and said, "Someday you
will have a pet of your own.
I know the kind you want.
Not too big!
Not too little!
Your pet must be just big enough!
Just big enough to play with you."

Days came and went, but there was
no pet for Honey.
At last she said, "Father forgets.
He forgets about getting a pet for me.
I'll have to find a pet of my own.
There are many kinds of animals
all around the farm.
I can find a pet if I look for one.
I'll put on my hat and look today."

Honey put on her big white hat.

She put on her new blue coat.

Then off she went to find a pet
of her own.

Soon Honey saw some little bluebirds.

But they flew too fast and too high
for her to catch one of them.

All at once she saw a pretty robin
in the grass along the fence.

"A robin likes to hop," said Honey.
"Maybe I can catch a robin."

But the robin saw her coming, and
it flew far away.

Honey ran after a fat gray mouse, but the mouse ran down into a hole.

"Oh!" said Honey. "A mouse can't be a pet because it lives in a hole."

Next she ran after a squirrel. But it went hurrying up a tree.

Then Honey ran after a rabbit.

She ran fast, but the rabbit ran faster.

All at once Honey's pretty hat fell off.

She stopped to get her hat. Then she saw that the rabbit had gone.

"Well, I'll catch some kind of pet," Honey said.

At last Honey came to some water.

"Fish!" she shouted. "I see fish!

I see pretty colored fish down here
in the water. I'll try to catch a fish.

A fish will make a good pet."

Splash, splash! Away went the fish.

Splash, splash went the water
all over Honey's hat and coat.

"Oh, dear! I can't catch a fish,"
she said.

"I can't catch a rabbit or a squirrel
or a mouse or a robin.

I can't get a pet of my own!"

On the way home Honey met her father coming from town.

She said, "Oh, Father, I wanted a pet.
I ran after a robin and a mouse.
I ran after a squirrel and a rabbit.
I splashed in the water for a fish.
But they all got away."

Then Father took something from his big coat pocket.

"A little white puppy!" shouted Honey.

"A little puppy with a black spot around one eye!

Oh, Father! You didn't forget.
You got me a pet after all.
A pet of my very own!"

Who Can Fool a Goat?

It was time for Halloween fun.

Bunny and Funny had on old coats
and hats of Father's.

Honey had on an old coat and hat
of Mother's.

"We don't look like us," laughed Honey.

"Puppy can't tell which is which."

"Well!" said Bunny. "We don't want
to look like us on Halloween.

We want to play tricks and fool people
on Halloween night."

All at once Puppy began to sniff.

He sniffed at Bunny.

He sniffed at Funny.

He sniffed and sniffed at Honey.

Then he jumped up on her.

"Bow-wow, bow-wow!" he said.

"Puppy knows me!" Honey said.

"I didn't fool him at all."

Just then Father came into the room.

"Hello, hello!" he laughed.

"Where are my three little girls going
on Halloween?"

"Father knows us!" said the girls.

"If we didn't fool Father and Puppy,
we can't fool other people.

We can't have fun on Halloween night."

"Yes, you can," said Father. "I know
how you can fool people on Halloween."

Father got some water and some paints.

Then he painted each little girl and made her look very funny.

Each girl had lines painted all around her eyes.

They each had blue spots of paint here and green spots there.

"Now we can fool people," said Honey. "We can fool John and Nancy Ann.

After dark we will go down the road to Hill Farm and fool them.

We can have Halloween fun when night comes."

It was getting dark when the sisters
went out the door that Halloween night.

Puppy was just coming in.

He looked at Honey.

He looked at Bunny.

He looked and looked at Funny.

"Bow-wow-wow," he said. Then he ran
into the house as fast as he could go.

The girls laughed and laughed.

"This is fun," said Bunny.

"Our spots of paint fooled Puppy."

All at once the girls heard a noise
in the barn.

Ee-ee! Ee-ee! Bang! Bang!

"Oh, dear me!" said Funny. "I know
who is making that noise.

Pony is hungry. That is the way he
tells me he wants something to eat."

Then the girls heard another noise.

Ba-a! Ba-a! Bump! Bump!

"Goat is hungry, too," said Bunny.
"He is making that noise."

Bang, bang, bang went Pony's feet
on the side of the barn.

Bump, bump, bump went Goat's head.

"Oh, let's hurry!" said Bunny.

"Both Goat and Pony are very hungry.

We must not forget to feed them
just because it is Halloween."

"Ba-a, ba-a!" said Goat when Bunny
opened the barn door.

Then he bumped her with his head.

He bumped her out into the barnyard,
and Bunny fell down.

Her sisters jumped up on the fence
so that Goat could not bump them.

"Oh, Bunny!" they called.

"Goat didn't know you. You fooled him!"

"Yes, I did," laughed Bunny. "But it
was not fun to fool Goat.

Goats don't know about Halloween.

They don't like to be fooled."

New Storybook Friends

Who Is Calling?

Ten hungry little chickens ran across
the chicken yard to their mother.

"What is it? What is it, Mother?"
peeped each wee chicken.

"Why did you call us?
What do you want?"

"Nothing, children! I didn't call you,"
clucked their mother in surprise.

"You called us," said the chickens.

"We heard you clucking."

Just then they all heard a funny noise.
Er-er-er-oo!

"That is Mr. Rooster," said a chicken.
"He is calling us."

All the hens and their chickens ran across the yard to Mr. Rooster.

"Why did you call us?" they asked.

The rooster looked surprised.

He said, "I didn't call. I was sleeping."

"Well, well!" clucked the hens.

"Tell us who was making that noise."

"I don't know," said the old rooster.

Then everyone heard another noise.

Me-ow, me-ow.

"A cat!" said the rooster.

"A hungry cat is making that noise.
He will catch each one of us."

They ran into the henhouse. Then they
peeped out to see if the cat was coming.

No cat came. So they ran out again.

As soon as they were all outside,
they heard a quacking noise.

"A duck is calling," said Mr. Rooster.

The rooster, the hens, and the chickens
ran to see what the ducks wanted.
"What do you want? Why did you
call us?" they asked their friends.

"We didn't call you," said the ducks.

Before they could say anything more,
they all heard the caw of a crow.

"That is old Mr. Crow," said a duck. "He is over there by the barn."

The ducks, the hens, the chickens, and the rooster ran across to the barn.

There sat Mr. Crow on the fence.

"What is it?" they asked him.

"What is what?" asked the crow.

"Why did you call us?" asked a hen.

"I didn't," the crow said.

The chickens, the hens, the ducks, and the rooster all looked surprised.

Each one said, "We heard you call."

High up in the tree a bird began
to call, "Ch-ee! Ch-ee!"

"That is Mr. Robin," said the crow.

Then the animals on the ground saw
that it was not Mr. Robin.

It was a catbird!

"Fooled!" quacked an old duck.

"Mr. Catbird was making all the noises
that fooled us. He thinks it is funny
to call like other animals and fool us.

He has fooled me before, but he can't
fool me again by that trick."

"Oh, no," said the rooster.

But he and the duck and their friends
thought it was a very good trick.

They wished they could make
more than one kind of noise.

120

Catching Tails

Small Gray Kitten was running
around after her long, pretty tail.

She was going around so fast that she
looked like a flying gray ball.

A fat brown puppy was sleeping
on a grassy spot by the barn door.

He opened one eye and looked
at the kitten.

"Why are you running around so fast?"
he asked her.

"Because I want to catch my tail,"
said Small Gray Kitten. "This is fun."

121

"Fun!" sniffed the puppy. "Then I'll see if it is fun for me."

So he got up and began running around after his little brown tail.

Old Billy Goat was eating grass along the fence. He looked at Puppy and asked, "Whatever are you doing?"

"Catching my tail," Brown Puppy said.

"But why?" asked the goat.

"Because Small Gray Kitten says that it is fun," said the puppy.

"Then I think I'll try it," said Billy.

So he began running around after his wee, short tail.

Sleepy Cow was standing in the field swishing her long red tail.

When she saw Billy, she said, "Moo! Whatever are you doing?"

"Catching my tail," said the goat.

"But why?" asked Sleepy Cow.

"Because I heard Fat Brown Puppy say that it is fun," the goat said.

"Then I'll try it," said the cow.

So she began running around.

Mr. Horse came galloping by.

"Whatever are you doing?" he asked.

"Moo, moo," said the cow. "I am trying to catch my tail.

Billy Goat says that it is fun."

"Well!" said the horse.

"If that is fun, I'll try it, too."

Then the horse began running around.

Soon Mr. Robin flew by.

He sat on top of the fence and looked
at the animals on the ground.

At last he asked, "Is that fun?"

"Well, no," said the horse.

"Galloping is more fun than this."

"Then why not gallop?" said the robin.

"I think I will," said the horse, and
off across the grassy field he went.

"Moo-oo," said the cow.

"Standing under a tree in a green field
is more fun than this."

And off she went to stand and swish
her tail in the grassy field.

Then Mr. Robin looked at the goat, who
was going around as fast as he could.

"Do you think you will ever catch
your wee, short tail?" asked the robin.

"No," said Billy. "But I am trying to.
Brown Puppy says it is fun."

"Is it?" asked the robin.

"No! It is more fun to eat grass,"
Billy said. And off he ran to eat some.

Mr. Robin saw the little puppy and
the kitten running after their tails.

"Go on," said the robin. "If you think
that is fun, just go on running. But you
will not catch your tails. Not ever!"

Just then Small Gray Kitten did it.

"Well!" said the robin as he flew off.

"At last you did catch your tail!
But whatever for? Whatever for?"

Little Rooster and the Sun

Once there was a little red rooster
who did not like the dark.

One morning he went to the barnyard
before the sun came up.

He flew up on the fence and looked
at the treetops far across the fields.
But he did not see the sun.

Little Rooster was not happy.

"I want the big yellow sun to hurry,"
he thought. "Maybe it will come up if I
tell it that I don't like the dark."

Little Rooster tried to talk to the sun.

He tried and tried to tell it to come up.
But when he opened his bill, he made
just a wee, wee noise.

"Er-er!" was all that he could say.

He tried and tried again.

At last he made a bigger noise.

At last he said, "Er-er-er-oo!
Er-er-er-oo!"

Just then Little Rooster saw the sun
coming up.

Up, up over the tops of the trees
it came.

"How wonderful!" said Little Rooster
as he jumped down on the ground.

"How wonderful I am!

I can wake the sun!"

He walked around the grassy barnyard
with his head very high.

He did not eat with the hens and
ducks and little chickens.

"Cluck, cluck, cluck!" said the hens.

"Quack, quack, quack!" said the ducks.

"Peep, peep, peep!" said the chickens.
"Why don't you eat your food?

Why do you stand here with your head
so high?"

Then Little Rooster shouted, "I have something wonderful to think about.

Early this morning I did something that is very wonderful."

"What did you do? Tell us about it," clucked the hens.

"No!" said the rooster. "Just wake up early in the morning, and you will see."

Next morning all the hens and ducks and little chickens got up early.

All of them ran out into the barnyard before the sun was up.

"How dark it is!" they said.

In a short time they saw Little Rooster come walking across the barnyard.

They saw him fly up to the top of the high fence and open his bill.

They heard him crow "Er-er-er-oo!"

Then up came the big yellow sun!

Up over the treetops it came.

"See!" said Little Rooster. "I said
I could do something wonderful, and
I did. I waked the big yellow sun!"

"So you did!" clucked the hens.

"So you did!" said all the others.

"Never, never have we seen anything
as wonderful as that.

We never have seen a rooster
as wonderful as you."

And to this very day all roosters crow
early in the morning.

They all crow just as the sun
comes up.

A Wonderful Name

All the Rabbit family were standing around their small new baby.

"Let's call him Bunny," said his father.

"No, no," said his mother.

"No, no, no," said his grandmother.

"Why not?" asked his grandfather.

"Because!" said Grandmother Rabbit. "Because every baby rabbit in the woods and fields is named Bunny.

Our baby must have a better name than any other baby rabbit.

He must have a name of his own."

Then old Grandfather Rabbit said,
"I am hungry. Let's eat dinner before
we think about names."

"No!" said Mother Rabbit.

"First we will think about names, and
then we will eat dinner."

They all sat down and began to think.

They thought of long names, and they
thought of short names. But no name
pleased Mother Rabbit.

At last the old grandfather jumped up.

"We never can think of a name that is
good enough for our baby!" he said.

"So I am going to the woods to visit
my friend, Mr. Ground Hog.

Maybe he can think of a good name."

Hop, hop, hop went the rabbit across
the field to visit his friend in the woods.

Soon old Grandfather Rabbit came
to a hole in a grassy hillside.

"Wake up, Mr. Ground Hog!" he said.
"I want you to come home with me and
see our new baby.

You never have seen a baby that is
as wonderful as he is. You must
help us think of a name for him."

Mr. Ground Hog came to his door.

Then he opened his eyes and saw that
the sun had not gone down.

"Oh, it is too early for a ground hog
to wake up," he said. "I'll not come out
and visit you before dark."

Three neighbors heard what the rabbit
was saying to Mr. Ground Hog.

Mrs. Brown Bear, Mrs. Squirrel, and
Mrs. Crow were the three neighbors.

Each one thought, "A baby rabbit
can't be as nice as my baby."

As Grandfather Rabbit went away,
each neighbor called to him.

Each one said, "I'll come at once
to visit the new baby rabbit.

I'll see if he is more wonderful than
any baby I have ever seen."

Then each neighbor walked out
of the woods and across the field.

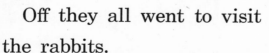

Off they all went to visit
the rabbits.

"Oh!" thought Mrs. Bear.

"This baby is not as big as my baby."

"Well, well!" thought Mrs. Squirrel.

"This baby rabbit has a very short tail.
It is not long like my baby's tail."

"My, my, my!" thought Mrs. Crow.

"This baby's coat is not very pretty.
It is not black like my baby's coat."

Then Mrs. Bear said, "This wee rabbit
looks just like any other rabbit.

A good name for this baby is Bunny."

"No!" said Mother Rabbit. "That is
not the name for my baby."

After the other animals had gone away,
Grandfather Rabbit said, "Oh, dear me!

If we don't think of a good name,
I'll never get any food.

It is time for Mr. Ground Hog to get up.
I'll go see if he can think of a name
that is nice enough for our baby."

Hop, hop, hop he went. But he met
the ground hog at the door.

"Hello," said the rabbit. "You came
just in time to name our _____."

But before he could say anything more,
his friend went inside to see the baby.

It looked like any other rabbit that
Mr. Ground Hog had ever seen. But he
did not say so.

He said, "What a wonderful baby!
See how he wiggles his wee nose."

"Oh!" shouted Grandfather Rabbit.
"Mr. Ground Hog has named our baby.
Wee Wiggle Nose is a nice name
for a rabbit who can wiggle his nose."

"Yes, it is!" said Mother Rabbit.
"It is a good name for our baby.
Every rabbit can wiggle its nose, but
not one is named Wee Wiggle Nose!"

Old Grandfather Rabbit began to hop
up and down.

"Thank you, Mr. Ground Hog," he said.
"At last our baby has a name!
Now I can eat my dinner!"

Little Bear and the Honey

One nice morning a little brown bear went out walking. He went walking away to the woods to see what he could see.

He looked first on one side of him and then on the other side.

All at once his little black nose went sniff, sniff!

"M-m-m! What a good smell!" he said. "It smells like honey, and I am going to find some for my dinner.

My nose will tell me which tree the honey is in."

Little Bear sniffed at each tree
as he went along.

At last he stopped under a big tree
and sniffed again.

"M-m!" he said. "I smell honey here.
My nose tells me that it is up
in this big tree."

Little Bear saw a round, dark hole
high up in the tree.

"Oh, oh!" he shouted. "I know where
the honey is! It is in that dark hole.

Honey is the best food there is, and
I'll climb up and get it."

Little Bear began to climb the tree
as fast as he could.

Little Bear climbed high, high up
to the round, dark hole.

As soon as he put his black nose
into it, out flew some bees!

More bees than he had ever seen!

They buzzed all around his head and
began to sting his little black nose.

Buzz, buzz! Sting, sting, sting!

Little Bear pulled his nose out
of the hole in a hurry.

Down that tree he climbed, and
out of the woods he ran.

By the time Little Bear got home,
there was a big puff on his nose.

When Mother Bear saw it, she said,
"I see that you tried to get some honey.
But you let the bees sting you."

"Oh, oh, oh!" said Little Bear.
"I'll never climb a honey tree again.
I don't want any more bee stings."

Mother Bear said, "I'll get something
to put on your nose. It will be better
very soon.

You will forget about the bee stings
when you smell honey again.

Next time you will get the honey."

A Pie for Billy Goat

Mother Pig and Jolly Little Pig lived
in a small white house in Animal Town.

In their yard was a big apple tree.
On the tree were the best apples in town.

One day Jolly Little Pig said, "I wish
I had a good apple pie. Why don't you
make one, Mother?"

"I'll make pies for dinner today,"
said Mother Pig. "But first I must go
to the store and buy some things."

She put on her coat and hat. Then she
went out with a big yellow basket.

Jolly Little Pig stayed at home.

Soon Red Cow and her wee calf came
and looked over the fence.

"Moo, moo! Moo, moo!" said Red Cow.
"What fine apples! Just smell them!
Let's take five or six."

"Please don't!" said the little pig.

"Mother is going to make apple pies,
and we must use all our apples.

If you will come back at six o'clock,
she will give each of you a nice pie."

"Moo, moo, thank you," said Red Cow.

Then she and her calf went on.

Next Gray Pony came galloping along.
He stopped at the tree and said,
"Ee-ee! What fine apples you have!

How good they smell! Please pull off
the best ones and give them to me."

"Oh, no, no!" said Jolly Little Pig.
"If I do that, my mother will not have
enough apples to make pies.

Just wait until six o'clock, and then
we will give you an apple pie."

"Fine!" said Gray Pony. "I'll be glad
to wait until six o'clock."

And the pony went galloping
down the road.

By and by Billy Goat stopped and said,
"What fine red apples!

I think I'll eat the biggest ones because
the biggest ones will be the best."

"Oh, please don't!" said Little Pig.

"Don't eat the apples now.

Mother is going to make apple pies,
and we must use all our apples.

Just wait until six o'clock, and then
you may have the biggest pie of all."

But Billy Goat did not wait.

Over the fence he jumped before
Jolly Little Pig could stop him.

Billy Goat ran at the apple tree and bumped it with his head. He bumped the tree until ten big apples fell off.

Then he ate all ten of them.

"See!" he said as he wiggled his nose and swished his short white tail.

"I ate all the apples I wanted, but I'll not forget about the pies. I'll visit you again at six o'clock.

When the apple pies are ready, I want the biggest and best one of all."

Then Billy Goat jumped over the fence and ran down the road.

When Jolly Little Pig saw his mother
coming home, he ran out and met her.

He began to tell her all about
Billy Goat and the apples.

"H-m-m!" said Mother Pig.

"Billy thinks he is very funny, but
I'll play a trick on him. I'll give him
a pie that he never will forget.

Just wait until six o'clock and see."

Then Mother Pig began making pies.

At six o'clock Red Cow was there with
her calf. So were Gray Pony and Billy.

"Are the pies ready?" they all asked.

"Yes, yes! Come in!" said Mother Pig.

"The pies are all ready for you."

"I am ready, too," shouted Billy Goat.

"I want the biggest pie of all, and
I see which one it is."

Billy began to eat the biggest pie.

All at once he shouted, "Oh! Oh! Oh!
My pie has no apples in it!

My pie is full of grass!"

"Yes, Mr. Billy! I know it is,"
said Mother Pig with a merry laugh.

"You ate your apples this morning."

"Oh, oh," laughed all the other animals.

"Billy knows which pie is biggest, but
he can't tell which pie is best."

"Ba-a-a!" shouted Billy Goat. "Ba-a!"

Out of Mother Pig's house he ran,
banging the door behind him.

The Candy Tree

It was early in the morning, and
Bobby Squirrel had just waked up.

He opened his sleepy eyes and wiggled
all over. Then he went back to sleep
in his big soft nest.

He did not wake up until the sun was
high overhead. Then he was hungry
and ready for his breakfast.

Down the tree he swished to look
for nuts on the ground.

Soon he heard some children making
a noise, and he saw them running.

All at once Bobby saw a boy drop
some little colored things.

What pretty colors they were!

Red, green, blue, and yellow!

They were small candy eggs, but Bobby
had never seen any eggs like them.

"Maybe they are bird eggs that have
colored paint on them," Bobby thought.

Then he sniffed at the eggs.

"M-m!" he said. "How nice they smell!
They smell better than nuts. I'll eat one
and see if it is better."

So Bobby ate one of the pretty eggs.

How soft and good it was!

It was much, much better than nuts.

Bobby ate one egg after another until there was just one egg on the ground.

"I'll not eat this one," thought Bobby.

"I'll show it to old Grandfather Squirrel. Maybe he can tell me what it is."

Old Grandfather Squirrel was sleeping when Bobby came to visit him.

"Good morning," said Bobby. "I want to show you something that I found. I ate some like it for breakfast, and I liked them much better than nuts. Do you know what kind of food it is? Do you know where I can get more?"

Sleepy old Grandfather Squirrel took the soft blue egg and sniffed at it.

"This smells like candy," he said.

"I have seen children eat candy, but I never knew where they got it."

Bobby sat there thinking and thinking.
At last he said, "Maybe candy grows
on trees, just the way nuts do.

I'll dig a hole in the ground and put
this candy egg in it. Maybe a candy tree
will grow here on this very spot.

Then I'll have all the candy I can eat."

He ran down the tree and began
to dig a hole in the ground.

Grandfather Squirrel saw Bobby dig
the hole, but he did not say anything.
He just laughed and laughed.

He knew that a tree could not grow
from candy. But it was a long time
before Bobby knew it.

Bunny Rabbit's Home

Bunny Rabbit and his mother liked
to eat cabbage. So their home was
a hole in a big cabbage field.

One day at breakfast Bunny said,
"I want a home of my own."

"Wait, Bunny," said his mother.

"Wait until you grow a little bigger."

Each day Bunny ate lots of cabbage.
He began to grow big and fat.

At last his mother said to him,
"Bunny, you are a big rabbit now.

You are big enough to dig a home
of your own. I'll show you how."

153

Then Mother Rabbit showed Bunny
where to make his home.

"Dig in this cabbage field," she said.
"Dig here by the side of the fence."

Bunny Rabbit thought he knew
all about making a home. So he
made a hole far down in the ground.

In it he put soft grass and lots
of leaves to sleep on.

"Now my home is ready," he said.

But Mother Rabbit knew better.

"No, no," she said. "A rabbit's home
must have two doors. And the back door
must be far away from the front door."

So Bunny made a back door that was
far away from his front door.

"Now, that is much better,"
said Mother Rabbit.

"Now you can use both doors.

You can go in through the front door
and come out through the back door.

Or you can go in through the back door
and come out through the front door."

Bunny sat there and wiggled his nose
for a long time. By and by he asked,
"Why must I use two doors?"

"Just wait," said Mother Rabbit.

"Someday you will know why."

The next morning Bunny was eating his breakfast in the cabbage field.

Hop, hop, hop went the hungry rabbit from one large cabbage to another.

Wiggle, wiggle went his soft nose as he ate the good green leaves.

All at once he heard a dog.

Bow-wow! Bow-wow! Bow-wow!

The dog was coming fast! Very fast!

But Bunny went faster!

His short white puff of a tail went through his front door just as the dog got there.

Sniff, sniff went the dog's nose.

"I can smell that rabbit in this hole,"
the dog thought. "I'll soon dig him out."

But Bunny did not stay in his home.

He ran out through his back door
as fast as he could run.

He never stopped running until he was
a long way from the cabbage field.

And he did not go back to his home
until the dog had gone far, far away.

Now at last Bunny knew why
a rabbit's home must have two doors.

That is one way a rabbit can fool
a dog.

Little Bear's Wish

One morning after breakfast Mrs. Bear
got ready to rake leaves.

She took Little Bear with her and
showed him how to rake.

Mrs. Bear had a large rake, and she
raked leaves very fast.

Little Bear had a short rake, and he
raked much slower than his mother did.

Slower and slower went his rake until
at last he let it drop.

"Why can't I do this work tomorrow?"
he asked his mother. "I don't want
to rake leaves today."

"Well, you can catch fish or get honey,"
said Mother Bear. "Fish or honey
will be fine for breakfast tomorrow."

But Little Bear said, "I splash water
in my eyes when I catch fish. The bees
sting me when I climb trees for honey."

Then Mother Bear thought of lots
of other things for Little Bear to do.

"You could read a storybook," she said.

"You could visit Baby Black Bear and
play games. Or you could play circus
with his new toy drum."

"No!" said Little Bear. "I have read
all my storybooks. I don't want to play
any games or play circus.

I want to do nothing. Just nothing."

"Well, well!" said Mother Bear.

"I'll have to think about that."

By and by Mother Bear said that
Little Bear could have his wish.

"Tomorrow is your birthday," she said.
"Tomorrow you can do what you please."

"How wonderful!" shouted Little Bear.
"That will be a wonderful birthday!
I'll wake up early tomorrow morning.
I'll have lots of time to do nothing."

Just as the sun came up next morning,
Little Bear went to the woods.

Soon he found a soft grassy spot
under a large tree.

"This is nice," he said. "I'll stay here
all day long and do nothing.
Just nothing!"

The wind made a soft swishing noise
as it blew through the woods.

It blew across the grass. And it blew
through the tree over Little Bear's head.

It blew and blew on Little Bear, who
sat under the large tree doing nothing.

By and by Little Bear got sleepy.

"Oh!" he said. "This is not much fun.

It makes me very tired to do nothing.
I wish I could think of something
that is more fun."

Just then Little Bear knew what he
wanted to do on his birthday.

Back through the woods he ran.

"Oh, Mother!" he said. "Now I want
to catch fish and get lots of honey."

But Mother Bear said, "I got honey
this morning, and Father got some fish."

"Oh, dear! Doing nothing makes me tired and sleepy," said Little Bear.

"Please think of something I can do.

I am so tired of doing nothing."

Mrs. Bear said, "Night is coming, and you must go to sleep now.

But you may work all day tomorrow and help us get ready for winter.

Tomorrow you may help your father dig a large winter home in the garden."

"Fine!" said Little Bear. "I will dig and dig and dig all day tomorrow."

The next day he was as busy as he could be. And he was very happy.

The Circus Parade

"Come! Come! Come!" called
a big, big drum.

"Get ready for the circus parade."

Baby Elephant heard the drum, and she
knew what the drum was saying. But she
did not get ready for the parade.

She was tired of being in a circus
and doing tricks.

She was tired of standing on her head.
She was tired of standing on two feet.

"I'll run far away from that old drum,"
thought Baby Elephant. But just then
she heard the drum again.

"Come! Come! Come!" called
the big, big drum.

"Get ready for the circus parade."

All the other animals were getting ready.
But Baby Elephant just said, "Don't talk
to me, Old Drum.

I don't like parades, and I don't like
the circus. I'll run away from the city
and find a place where I can hide."

So Baby Elephant ran away to look
for a place where she could hide.

Soon Baby Elephant came to a garden,
where she met a mouse.

"Hello," said the elephant. "This is
a wonderful place to hide. I think I'll
stay in this garden forever."

"Then help me pick cabbages and corn
before the snow comes," said the mouse.

"We can't find any food in the garden
when the snow comes. So we must
be ready for winter.

You had better think about that."

"Good-by!" called Baby Elephant.

"I can't live in this garden because
I don't want to pick cabbages and corn."

Before long, Baby Elephant stopped
in a park, where she met a squirrel.

"Hello," she said. "I like this place.
I think I'll stay here forever."

"Then you must start to pick up lots
of nuts," said the squirrel.

"Why?" asked Baby Elephant.

"Because we must be ready for winter,"
said the squirrel. "When the snow comes,
we can't find any food on the ground.
You had better think about that."

"Good-by!" called Baby Elephant.

"I'll not stay another minute because
I don't want to pick up nuts."

Baby Elephant went on until she saw
a horse standing in a grassy field.

"Hello," she said. "I like this place.
I think I'll hide here forever."

"Then start at once to cut some grass,"
said the horse. "We must put grass
in the barn before the snow comes.

We can't find any grass to eat when
the snow is on the ground. So we
must get ready for winter.

You had better think about that."

Baby Elephant said, "I am thinking
about it this very minute, Mr. Horse.

I'll not stay here and cut grass."

Soon Baby Elephant came to the woods.

There she met a brown bear, who was
making a hole in the ground.

"Hello," said the elephant. "This is
a wonderful place to hide from the circus.
I think I'll stay here forever."

"Then don't stand here and talk,"
said the bear. "You must start to dig
a large hole in the ground."

"Why?" asked Baby Elephant.

"Because you must sleep in a hole
all winter just as I do," said the bear.

"If you want to live here in the woods,
you must sleep in a hole all winter.

You had better think about that."

All at once Baby Elephant heard
the circus drum again.

Then she said, "I don't want to live
in a garden or park or field or woods.

I don't want to pick cabbage and corn.
I don't want to hide nuts or cut grass
or sleep in a hole in the ground.

The circus is the best place for me."

So she called to the big, big drum,
"Wait for me! Here I come!"

She ran back to the circus as fast
as she could. And she got there
just in time.

She was in time to be in the parade.

Mrs. Goose Has a Party

Just after breakfast one Saturday,
Mrs. Goose thought of something.

"I'll have a party," she said.

"I think I'll have it today.

Saturday is a good day for a party
because this is the day I bake pies.

I'll have the party at four o'clock.

I'll ask Mrs. Red Hen, Mrs. Squirrel,
Mrs. Rabbit, and The Three Ducks.

I must hurry, hurry, hurry!

I have lots and lots of work to do."

Just then Mrs. Goose looked up and
saw that it was after ten o'clock.

"Me, oh, my!" she said to herself.
"The morning will soon be gone!

I must start this very minute and
clean my house before I bake the pies."

So she started to clean her house.

She worked and worked and worked.

"There! It is clean!" she said at last.
"Every room is as clean as can be.

Now I'll bake some pies. I'll bake
some cookies, too.

Everyone likes my good apple pies and
my milk-and-honey cookies."

171

It was one o'clock when Mrs. Goose started to bake pies and cookies.

First she cut up apples. Next she got the honey and milk and eggs ready.

"Oh, me! Oh, me! Oh, my!" she said. "I must hurry, or my cookies and pies will never be baked by four o'clock."

Mrs. Goose worked fast. So she had everything ready in time for the party.

Then she was very, very tired.

"I think I'll sit down for a minute," she said to herself. But as soon as she sat down, she went to sleep.

In ten minutes Mrs. Goose waked up.

"Oh, my! Oh, me!" she thought.

"It soon will be four o'clock!

I must hurry, hurry, hurry and put on
my best clothes. I must be ready
for my own party."

She put on her very best clothes, and
then she looked at herself.

"How fine I look!" she thought.

"I know I am the best-looking goose
in Animal Town."

It was just four o'clock, and
all the pies were baked and cut.
The honey cookies were ready, too.

The small house was very clean, and
Mrs. Goose had on her very best clothes.

"Now I'll sit down," she thought.

"I'll sit down until my friends come."

Mrs. Goose sat there all by herself
until five o'clock.

"Oh, me! How late my friends are!"
she said. "Will they ever come?"

All at once Mrs. Goose heard the wind.
Oo-oo! How it blew!

She went to the door and looked out.

"It is raining!" she said to herself.

"No one will come out in the wind and
the rain. But I'll sit down and wait
for my friends anyway."

At ten minutes after five Mrs. Goose
got up and looked out again.

She saw The Three Ducks splashing
through the water in the road.

Behind them came three blue umbrellas.
Under the umbrellas were Mrs. Rabbit,
Mrs. Red Hen, and Mrs. Squirrel.

They were all in line, just like a parade.

"Honk, honk, honk!" called Mrs. Goose.
"You are late!"

"Late?" quacked The Three Ducks.
"Late for what?"

"Late for my party!" called Mrs. Goose.

Then all six of the animals shouted,
"Party! You didn't ask us to a party.
Did you forget to ask us?"

Mrs. Goose looked surprised.

"Oh!" she said. "Maybe I did forget.
I was so busy cleaning my house and
making my cookies and pies!"

"Oh, well," quacked the ducks.

"We are late, but we will be glad
to come anyway."

"Yes, yes, come in," honked Mrs. Goose.
"Please come in and sit down."

So they went inside, and Mrs. Goose
had a good party after all.

Work on Pleasant Street

Zeke and His Saw

One day Tommy saw Zeke coming with his saw.

Zeke was the man who helped the people on Pleasant Street.

"Hello, Zeke," said Tommy. "Are you going to make our garden fence today? If you are, I want to help."

"Fine! Fine!" said Zeke. "Just wait a minute until I get my horses."

"Horses!" said Tommy. "Must we have horses to make a fence?"

"Wait and see," laughed Zeke.

When Zeke came back, Tommy said,
"Where are your horses?"

"Here they are," said Zeke as he put
two funny-looking things on the ground.

"Why, Zeke!" said Tommy. "They don't
look like horses! They can't help you
build a fence."

"They are sawhorses," said Zeke.
"They help my saw do its work."

Then he picked up a long stick of wood
and put it across the sawhorses.

"Now!" Zeke said. "You can see
how my saw and I build a fence."

Zeke took his saw in one hand.

He put his other hand on the stick.

Z-z-z-z-z! Z-z-z-z-z! sang the saw
as it went through the wood.

Then one long stick was two short ones.

Zeke took another long stick of wood
and sawed through it.

Then he sawed another and another.

Tommy put them in a pile. He piled
the sticks as fast as Zeke sawed.

Soon Zeke said, "Now, Tommy, let's see
if you can saw. I'll show you how."

Zeke put his hand over Tommy's
and said, "Now push this way.

Push and pull the saw just so.

Not too fast! Not too slow."

Soon Tommy was sawing all by himself.

Z-z-z-z-z! sang the saw as it cut
the sticks of wood.

All at once it made a funny noise.

"Stop! Stop! Not so fast!" said Zeke.
"You must take better care of my saw."

Then Tommy made the saw go slower.

Push—pull! Push—pull! it went
until the stick was sawed in two.

Tommy and Zeke worked all morning.
Sometimes Zeke sawed, and Tommy
piled the sticks. Sometimes Tommy
sawed the sticks, and Zeke piled them.

"This is a good start," said Zeke.
"Tomorrow we will build the fence."
Next morning they began very early.
Before night they had made a fence.

"Well, Zeke," said Tommy, "you and I
and the horses can build a good fence."

"Don't forget about the saw," said Zeke.
"You and I and the horses helped
this fine saw build a fence."

Bobby's New Friends

Bobby Bell was peeping through
the fence into Mr. Jolly's garden.

He could see two boys there.

Each one had a shovel in his hand.

Each one was digging in the ground.

"Oh, how I wish I knew what they
are digging!" thought Bobby.

But he did not ask, because he was
a new boy on Pleasant Street.

He thought that the boys in the garden
did not care to talk to him.

Soon Bobby saw one boy drop his shovel
and pick something up. Then he said,
"Look here in my hand, Jim.

This is bigger than the first one."

Bobby wanted to say, "Hello, boys!
What did you find?"

But he was afraid to say it. He was
afraid the boys would not talk to him.

"I'll get my shovel and start digging,"
Bobby said to himself. "Maybe I can
dig up something in my own garden."

He ran into the house and came out
with a small shovel in his hand.

Bobby started to dig all by himself.
Down into the ground went his shovel.

Soon Bobby heard the boys talking
on the other side of the fence.

"Look, Jim!" called Joe.

"I found a bigger one!"

Bobby could not wait another minute
to see what the boys had found.

He did not care about being afraid now.
So he ran over to the fence and asked,
"What is it? What did you find?"

The boys looked up from their digging.

"Come over here and see," they called.

Joe and Jim were digging potatoes, and they had a big pile of them.

"We are going to bake them," said Joe.

"Mr. Jolly said that we could have all the potatoes we could find here.

We are going to bake potatoes when we burn the leaves in our yards. But it is a surprise. Don't tell anyone."

"I can help you dig," said Bobby.

"Fine!" said both boys at once.

Bobby started digging and found six big potatoes all by himself.

"Oh, you have found one that is bigger than any of ours," said Jim. "You found the biggest one of all!"

The Big Surprise

It was the time for leaves to fall, and
down on the ground they came.

Brown and yellow leaves were falling
in all the yards on Pleasant Street.
Leaves were falling on all the walks
and on the city streets.

The wind blew the leaves all about, and
children's feet ran swishing through them.

Swish, swish, swish went the feet
all the way to school and back again.

When every yard was full of leaves,
Zeke would come to rake them.

All the fathers worked downtown.
So they were glad to pay Zeke to do
this work. And Zeke was glad to do it.

One day after school the children said,
"We will help you today, Zeke!"

"Fine!" said Zeke. "I can use a lot
of help when leaves are falling.

Now watch how I rake."

First he had to show the best way
to do it. So he raked by himself.

He started at Patty's house and raked
the leaves in long lines across the yard.

Next Zeke swished his big rake down
a line of leaves to make a pile.

The children watched until they knew
how to do it. Then they began to work.

At last all the leaves in all the yards
were piled up.

"Now the leaves are ready for us
to take away and burn," Zeke said.

"We are going to burn all of them
in Mr. Jolly's garden."

They took the leaves to the garden
in wagons and baskets.

Zeke got there first and put his leaves
on a pile of old bricks. Then he said,
"Let's make the fire here on the bricks."

"Oh, Zeke," said Bobby Bell, "may we
start the fire now?"

"No," said Zeke. "Not until dark."

After dark everyone on Pleasant Street
came out, and Zeke started the fire.

"I'll take care of the fire," he said.
"You people just stand there and watch."

"M-m-m-m!" said Mrs. Hill as she
smelled the burning leaves. "This is
a good smell."

After the fire had gone out, Zeke said,
"Now! Get ready for a big surprise."

He raked the burned leaves away from
the bricks and pushed the bricks away.
Then he called Joe and Jim and gave
each boy a long stick.

The people watched as the boys
raked out some round black things.

"Baked potatoes!" everyone shouted.
"Zeke put potatoes under the bricks!"

There were baked potatoes for everyone.
Potatoes for the children and the fathers
and mothers. Potatoes for Zeke and
Mrs. Hill, and some for Mr. Jolly.

But the biggest one of all was
for the new boy on Pleasant Street.

"M-m-m!" Bobby said. "It would be fun
to bake potatoes every night."

"Yes," laughed Zeke, "but I am afraid
we never could rake enough leaves."

The Biggest Apple

Early in the fall the apple tree
in Billy's yard was full of apples.

After school one day some boys came
with a basket to help pick the apples.

"Eat all you want," Billy told the boys.
"The apples you eat will be your pay
for picking them."

"Oh!" said Jack as he climbed the tree.
"We won't want any better pay."

The boys picked until dark, and they
picked before school the next morning.

"We won't pick the apples at the top
of the tree," Billy said.

"Father is afraid for us to climb
that high. He pays Zeke to climb up
to the top and pick the apples there."

Soon Billy saw his sister starting
to school. So he told the boys to take
some apples and hurry to school.

"We don't want to be late," he said.

Just then an apple fell off the tree.

Down it fell into a basket.

The boys saw the apple drop. It was
the biggest apple they had ever seen.

Each boy wanted it, but Billy was
the one who took it.

The other boys took some apples and
ran off to school. All their pockets
were full of nice red apples. Their hands
were full, too.

Billy just stayed there trying to get
the big apple into his pocket.

He tried and tried, but that big apple
would not go into his small side pocket.

His back pocket was bigger. So Billy
tried to push the apple into that one.

At first the apple would not go in.
But Billy gave it another big push.
At last it was in the pocket.

Billy ran all the way to school because
he was afraid he would be late.

But Billy was not late. He heard
the second bell just as he came
to his room.

After the children sat down, they sang.

Then Miss Gray told them a story, but Billy never heard the story. He was trying to do something about the apple.

It made a big bump in his pocket, and he could not sit up very well.

Soon the children opened their books and began to do their school work.

But Billy could not read his book. He was busy trying to get the apple out of his pocket.

Now Billy was sorry that he had ever seen that big apple.

Billy wiggled this way and that way
until he saw Miss Gray watching him.
He tried not to wiggle again. But he
just had to get that apple out somehow.

The second time that Miss Gray looked
at Billy, he told her about the apple.

"I am sorry," he said. "But the apple
won't come out. Can you help me?

You may have to cut my pocket, but
I don't care."

"Oh!" Miss Gray said. "I won't cut
your pocket. I'll just cut the apple."

So Miss Gray cut it and took it out.

Then no one could call it
the biggest apple again.

Who Cleaned the Walk?

One cold Saturday morning Peter and
his sister got up early.

They were very sleepy until they looked
out the window. Then the children gave
a glad shout.

"Snow fell last night!" they said.

"Winter has come!"

Through the front window they saw
soft white snow on the ground. It was
on the trees and on top of the houses.

"Look!" said Ellen. "See the holes
in the snow. Father's feet made them
when he went to town this morning."

Mother came to the window and said,
"See all the snow on the walk!

Grandmother is coming at ten o'clock
to visit us. We can't let her walk
through that deep, cold snow."

Ellen said, "Why don't you call Zeke?
He will shovel the snow off the walk."

"I telephoned to Zeke," said Mother.

"But other people had telephoned, too.
Zeke must take care of their walks first.
He won't get here before ten o'clock."

Then Peter thought of something.

"I'll shovel the snow," he said.

"I am sorry, Peter," said Mother.

"But you are too small. The shovel is
too large, and the snow is too deep.

Come away from the window and
eat breakfast. Then you may go outside."

198

After breakfast the children heard Zeke
in Dick's front yard. They called to him.
But Zeke was making a lot of noise, and
he never heard them call.

Zeke always sang when he worked,
and he always sang about himself.

The faster Zeke worked, the faster
he sang.

> "In the cold, cold winter
> Zeke shovels the snow.
> The deep, deep snow.
> In the cold, cold winter
> Zeke shovels the snow."

Peter and Ellen made a ball of snow and pushed it down the walk.

The ball got much bigger as they pushed it through the deep, soft snow.

Soon they pushed the big snowball out into the yard. Then they began to push a second ball of snow down the walk.

The children wanted Zeke to watch them make the snowball. But he did not stop his work.

Zeke just shoveled and sang as fast as he could! He made the snow fly high as he sang about himself and his work.

"Look, Zeke!" shouted Ellen.

"See our funny, fat snow man.

We gave him a big white hat."

Zeke came and looked over the fence.

"Of all things!" he said. "Who cleaned
your walk?"

Then Mother opened a window and
called to the children.

"How did you ever clean the walk?"
she asked.

"Oh, we didn't clean it," said Ellen.

"Our big snow man cleaned the walk.

Our snow man did it all by himself."

The Christmas Tree

In winter, children on Pleasant Street
played in Evergreen Park. They could
play all kinds of games there.

No one ever got in their way.

No one ever told them that they made
too much noise.

They always had fun in the big park.
But they thought they had more fun
in winter than at any other time.

In wintertime there always was a lot
of deep, clean snow in the park. So it
was a good place for winter fun.

Four days before Christmas some girls
were looking at a large evergreen tree.

"That large green tree looks just like
a Christmas tree," said Sally May.

"Oh, no," said Patty. "Christmas trees
always have pretty lights. They have
lots and lots of pretty colored lights!"

Jill said, "Maybe we could tie strings
of lights on this tree. Then it would be
a Christmas tree.

Then we would have a fine surprise
for all the people on Pleasant Street."

Just then the children saw Big Bill
and told him about the Christmas tree.

"That is fine," he said. "But the man
who takes care of the park must know
what you want to do. I'll see him and
tell him all about it today.

You must ask your fathers to help you
put the strings of lights on the tree."

Jill said, "We are sorry, but this is
a surprise. We can't ask our fathers."

The children thought for a second, and
then Susan said, "I'll telephone Zeke!"

Then she hurried away.

The next day after school, Zeke met the children in Evergreen Park.

They had brought six strings of lights.

"Six strings won't make much light," Zeke said. "We must try to get more if we want a beautiful Christmas tree."

"I know it," said Joe. "But we don't have any money to buy more lights."

Then along came Big Bill with strings of pretty lights in his hands.

He gave them to the children and said, "I brought all the colored lights I had. I am sorry that I didn't have more."

Then Big Bill stayed to help string the lights on the tree.

When the Christmas tree was ready,
everyone went home to eat dinner.

Zeke ate his dinner. Then he hurried
to a store to get something for the tree.

It was something that would surprise
the children. So he wanted to put it up
by himself before anyone came
to watch him.

All the children were busy at home.
They were telling everyone that they
had a beautiful surprise in the park.

They told their fathers and mothers.

They telephoned to Uncle Peter and
Miss Gray and all the other neighbors.

"Merry, merry Christmas!" they said
to each friend and neighbor.

"Please come out to Evergreen Park
right after dinner. Try not to be late."

That night everyone hurried to the park
on Pleasant Street. All the children and
their fathers and mothers came.

Uncle Peter was there, and so were
Miss Gray, Mrs. Hill, and the milkman.

Big Bill came and brought his family.

When the people saw the tree with
its colored lights, they gave a big shout.

"Oh, how beautiful!" everyone said.

"What a beautiful, beautiful tree!"

At that second, Patty shouted, "Look!
Look at the top of the tree!"

There was a beautiful light at the top
of the Christmas tree. Right under it
was Zeke's head.

"Oh," he said, "you came too soon, or
I came too late. I don't know which.

I brought just one more pretty light
for the Christmas tree. I wanted to put
it up when no one was here to see me."

All the people laughed and called,
"Merry, merry Christmas, Zeke!

Thanks for the beautiful light."

And everyone thought, "What would
we do if we didn't have Zeke?"

Zeke Makes Gardens

One nice spring day Dick and Jane
saw Zeke making Mrs. Hill's garden.

"Oh, Zeke," called Dick. "We want
to help put the seeds in the ground."

But Zeke said, "Why don't you make
a small garden of your own this spring?"

"We will," said both children at once.
"We will buy the seeds right now."

"Not so fast!" Zeke told them.

"Stay here and watch for a minute.
I'll show you how to make a garden."

Next day Zeke helped Dick and Jane
get ready to plant their seeds.

He put two sticks in the ground and
tied a string to them. Then he said,
"Plant the seeds along this string.

Don't plant them on top of the ground,
or they will blow away. Don't plant them
too deep, or they won't come up."

"We will do it right, Zeke," said Jane.
"It will be lots of fun to watch our seeds
grow into plants."

The next morning a nice spring rain
began to fall. As soon as it stopped,
Dick and Jane saw Zeke coming.

"Hello," said Zeke. "That spring rain
will make your seeds grow into plants.

I always say there is nothing better
than spring rain to make plants grow."

"But Zeke!" said both children.
"The birds are picking our seeds
out of the ground with their bills.

We won't have any plants."

Zeke hurried to the garden to see
those hungry birds eating the seeds.
But the birds flew away when they
saw Zeke.

Zeke said, "I must scare those birds and make them stay away."

Jane said, "Put bricks over the seeds and hide them from the birds."

"Oh, no," said Zeke. "Seeds can't grow under bricks. I'll just have to think of something better than bricks."

At last Zeke thought of something.

He brought a long stick and pushed it into the ground. He put a short stick right across the long stick.

Then he brought an old coat and a hat and put them over the sticks. Next he put a handkerchief in the coat pocket.

Last of all Zeke tied some little bells on strings and put them on the coat tails.

"Why, Zeke!" shouted Dick and Jane. "You have made a scarecrow!"

All at once the wind began to blow.

The scarecrow's clothes began blowing
in the wind. Then the bells on the coat
began making a big noise.

As Zeke and the children walked away,
the birds hurried back to the garden.

But the blowing coat and handkerchief
scared the birds. The noise of the bells
scared them, too.

"See those birds go," laughed Zeke.

"The flying clothes and that noise will
scare them every time the wind blows.
Now the seeds can grow into plants."

Tommy's Spring Work

Patty and her friend Ellen were playing in Patty's back yard one spring day.

"Tommy, come and play," called Patty.

But Tommy shook his head and said, "Not today! I have to help Zeke today. He says it is time for spring cleaning.

As soon as Zeke cleans the windows, I'm going to help him clean the yard. It is full of sticks and strings.

Next I'll help Jim and Uncle Peter paint the back fence."

"I am sorry, girls," said Uncle Peter.
"But I'll have to ask you to move.

We can't paint all the fence until you
move those toys away.

Tommy will help you move them."

Tommy brought his wagon and piled
the playthings in it. He moved them
to the front yard under a tree.

"Thank you, Tommy," said the girls.

"Now!" said Tommy. "I'm ready
to help do all the spring work.

Now I can help clean the yard and
help Uncle Peter paint the fence."

Soon the girls heard a buzzing noise coming near them. It was Zeke starting to cut the grass.

When he cut the grass, he always sang. He sang about himself and his work. This is what he sang.

> "Zeke cuts the grass,
>
> The long green grass.
>
> Zeke cuts the grass
>
> In the spring."

When Zeke came near the two girls, he said, "I'm sorry, but you must move. I have to cut the grass here."

Then Zeke saw Tommy near the fence.

"Oh, Tommy," he called. "Please help Patty and Ellen move their playthings."

Tommy brought his wagon and piled the playthings in it again. Then he began to pull it across the yard.

"Pull, pull!" said Tommy to himself.

"All I do is pull the wagon here and pull the wagon there."

Just as Tommy went by, Zeke called, "Thanks for helping me."

Tommy shook his head. Then he said, "No, no, Zeke! I'm not helping you. I'm always busy helping the girls move.

I have to move all their things from one place to another.

I'm sorry, but I don't have any time to help you. No time at all."

"Why, Tommy!" said Zeke. "You are helping me now. You help me when you move those toys out of my way."

"Do I, Zeke?" asked Tommy.

"Oh, my, yes," said Zeke.

Then he began to cut the grass again, and he sang about his work again.

As Tommy hurried across the yard with his wagon, he sang, too.

This is what he sang.

"Tommy pulls the wagon,
The red and yellow wagon.
Tommy helps Zeke
In the spring."

I Won't Forget

Ann was feeding Dick's rabbit when Zeke came walking through the yard.

"Hello, Zeke," called Ann.

"Come and see my beautiful rabbit."

Zeke shook his head and said, "My! That looks like Dick's Bunny Boy!"

"Yes, Zeke," Ann said, "you are right. But I'm going to take care of him now.

Dick and his family have gone to visit his grandmother. I'm going to take care of this rabbit until Dick comes home."

"Well, Ann," said Zeke, "try to take good care of Bunny Boy.

Some children will feed a pet one day and forget all about it the next day. But Dick always feeds Bunny every day.

Every morning he gives cabbage leaves to that rabbit to make him grow fat.

Every day Dick cuts grass for him.

Every morning Dick gives Bunny Boy some water and cleans his house.

I never would be afraid to let Dick take care of one of my rabbits.

If I had any rabbits!"

Ann shook her head at Zeke.

"I won't forget about Bunny," she said.

"I'll feed him every day and keep him nice and fat.

I'll be just like Dick."

For five days Ann did not forget.
But on Saturday her family was going
to take a boat ride with her grandfather.

When Ann got up on Saturday,
she was thinking of the boat ride.

At breakfast she talked about
the boat every minute.

After breakfast she thought about it
as she helped get a basket of food ready.

Soon the basket was full. Then Father
put it in the car.

"Hurry!" he called. "We don't want
to be late and miss the boat."

So the family got into the big blue car
and hurried off.

Soon they saw the boat in the water.

"Well, here we are!" Grandfather said. "I'll leave the car here near the water until we come back from the boat ride."

"My!" said Ann. "Won't it be nice to eat our dinner on the boat!"

Then she thought about the rabbit.

"Oh, dear!" she said to herself.

"I didn't feed Bunny Boy or give him any water this morning.

I don't want to miss the nice boat ride. But I just can't let Bunny Boy stay at home all day with no food."

When the car stopped, Ann said,
"I must go right back home!"

"Why? Why?" asked everyone.

"I didn't give Dick's rabbit any food
or water this morning," answered Ann.
"I'll go back on the streetcar and feed him.

I'm sorry to miss the nice boat ride
and all the fun, but I must go back."

Grandfather shook his head and said,
"No, Ann! You won't miss the fun, and
Dick's rabbit won't miss its breakfast.

I'll take you home and wait for you
until you feed the rabbit.

I'll ask the man who runs the boat
to keep it waiting for us."

So back they all went to Dick's house.

Ann jumped out of the car and hurried
into the yard by herself.

There was the white rabbit eating
cabbage leaves, and Zeke sat near it.

He was watching the rabbit wiggle
its soft little nose as it ate.

"Oh, Zeke!" said Ann. "I did forget
to feed the rabbit. I'm sorry."

"I'm not sorry," Zeke said. "I'm glad
you thought about Bunny and came back.

Now I know you always will feed him.
Now I won't ever be afraid to let you
keep one of my rabbits.

If I ever have any rabbits!"

The Big Shovel

"Oh, look!" Peter and Ellen called
when their father came home one day.

"See that big thing going by!
What is it? Where is it going?"

"It is a big shovel," answered Father.

"I don't know where it is going, but
get in and we will find out. We will
keep behind the shovel until it stops.

Then we will see where it is going."

The children climbed into the car, and
they all started after the shovel.

"This is like a parade," said Ellen.

"The big, slow shovel is in front, and
a car full of people is right behind it.
Our car is next, and four more cars
are coming behind us.

Turn around and look, Peter.

Turn around and look at the parade."

Peter turned around and said,
"Yes, it is like a parade.

That big, big shovel makes me think
of a big, slow elephant in a circus parade.
I'm going to call it Old Elephant Shovel."

The big shovel came to a place where
there were no houses at all. Then it
turned off on a grassy place and stopped.

All the other cars went on, but Father
turned off the street and stopped his car.

He said, "Let's stay here and watch
the shovel work. It is digging a hole
in the ground."

As Peter and his sister watched it dig,
their eyes got bigger and bigger.

"What is the hole for?" asked Ellen.

"Oh," answered Father, "when the hole
is big enough and deep enough,
someone will build a house over it."

All next day Old Elephant Shovel
went on digging.

When Father took the children back
to see it, the hole was much bigger.

"Oh," said Ellen, "will people build
a house right over the shovel? Will it
always stay in the hole?"

Then Peter said, "That is just what
I want to know, too.

Old Elephant Shovel digs himself in,
but how can he get himself out?"

"Just wait," answered Father.

"Wait until tomorrow! Then you will
see how the big, slow shovel gets out."

When they all went back the next day, the hole was bigger. It was deep, too.

Peter said, "Elephant Shovel is slow, but he can do a lot of work.

Soon the people can build the house."

"Oh, dear!" said Ellen.

"Now I'm afraid the big, slow shovel will never get out. He can't jump out, and he can't fly out of that deep hole."

"No!" said Peter. "He is so large that no one can ever get him out. The people will have to build the house over him."

By and by the hole was big enough and deep enough. The shovel stopped digging for a minute or two. Then it turned and started to dig again.

"Now!" said Father. "Watch and see the shovel get out."

"Look at the shovel now," said Ellen. "It is making the hole bigger than ever."

"No, no, Ellen," said her father as he shook his head.

"Old Elephant Shovel is digging a road up one side of the hole. That is how he will get himself out."

"Oh," laughed Peter, "nothing can keep Old Elephant Shovel down in a hole.

He digs himself in, and then he digs himself out!

No one can build a house over him."

Old
Storybook
Friends

The Boy and His Goats

Once there was a little boy who had three fine goats. And every morning he took them up a green hill to eat grass.

One day the boy was tired and sleepy. But when he went to sleep, his goats ran into a cornfield.

By and by the boy waked up and saw them eating the corn.

First he called to the goats. Then he ran into the field after them.

But the goats would not come out.

Then the little boy put his hands over his eyes and began to cry.

Soon Brother Rabbit came along.

"Why are you crying?" he asked.

"Oh!" said the boy. "I cry because
I can't get my goats out of the field."

The rabbit said, "Don't cry, little boy.
I'll show you how to get those goats
out of the cornfield."

Away the rabbit ran after the goats.
He ran and ran. But the three goats
would not come out of the cornfield.

The rabbit got very tired of running.
So he turned around and came back.

Then he began to cry.

He cried, and he cried, and he cried.

By and by a red fox came along.

"Well, Brother," he said, "why do you
sit there and cry?"

"Oh," answered the rabbit, "I'm crying
because the boy is crying.

The boy is crying because he can't get
his goats out of the cornfield."

Then the fox said, "Crying won't help.
I'll get those goats out of the field."

The fox galloped into the field, but he
could not make those goats come out.

Soon he turned around and came back.
Then he began to cry.

He cried, and he cried, and he cried.

Next a merry little honeybee flew by.

"Well, well, Brother Fox," said the bee. "Why do all of you sit there crying?"

"Oh," answered the fox, "I cry because Brother Rabbit is crying.

He is crying because the boy is crying.

The boy is crying because he can't get his goats out of the cornfield."

"Don't cry, Brother Fox," said the bee. "Crying won't get all those goats out. Watch me! I'll make them come out."

"How?" asked the crying fox.

"How can a little bee do something that a boy and a rabbit and a fox can't do?"

"Watch! I'll show you," said the bee.
"The goats are afraid of my sting."

Z-z-z, z-z-z buzzed the little bee as it
flew into the biggest goat's hair.

The big goat shook himself and tried
to make the bee go away. But it stayed
in his hair and began to sting.

The sting scared the goat, and he made
so much noise that he scared the others.
Then all three goats ran out of the field
and went galloping down the grassy hill.

They never stopped until they were
all the way down the hill and
home again.

Fooling the Cats

At one time a family of cats worked
for three roosters who lived together.
The cats brought food to the roosters
and wood for their chimney fire.

Sometimes the cats got very tired.

Then the roosters would say,
"The red on top of our heads is fire.
Do as we say, or we will burn the hair
off your beautiful tails."

The cats went on working because they
did not want to have their hair burned.

At night the cats went home to sleep. One night when they went home, they found their own chimney cold and black.

"My, my!" said Mother Cat. "We must get some fire for the chimney place."

She gave some straw to a little kitten and said, "Go to those roosters at once. Take this straw and put it near the fire on a rooster's head.

Then pull the straw away and blow on it to make the fire burn.

But watch out! Try to keep the hair on your tail away from the fire."

The kitten ran to the roosters' house and peeped into the room.

Two of the roosters had gone out, but the third one was sleeping.

The kitten went in and put the straw up to the sleeping rooster's red top.

After the kitten pulled the straw from
the third rooster's head, he started home.

He had to keep watching his tail to see
that the hair did not burn. But soon he
saw that the straw was not burning.

"I didn't blow on the straw," he said.
"Now I must go back a second time.

This time I'll blow on the straw
until it is on fire."

The kitten ran back and put the straw
up to the rooster's head a second time.

He blew and blew until he was tired.
But the straw would not catch fire.

When the kitten got home, his mother saw that he had no fire.

"The roosters scared you away before you could blow on the straw," she said. "Come with me, and I will do it!"

So the mother cat and the kitten ran to the roosters' house together.

The two roosters had not come home, but the third was sleeping as before.

The mother cat put the straw up near the third rooster's head. Then she pulled the straw away and blew on it.

She blew and blew, but the straw would not catch fire.

The cat looked at the third rooster again.
She saw that his red top was not fire.
It was just the color of fire.

She was not afraid of the rooster now.
She shook him and said, "Go to work!
We cats won't work for you any more."

The third rooster waked up and said,
"I'll burn the hair off your tail!"

"Oh, you can't scare me," said the cat.
"You have no fire to burn me."

After that day no cat has ever worked
for a rooster. And no rooster
has ever scared a cat.

How Man Made a Friend

Once all the dogs and the foxes called
each other Brother. And all of them
lived together in the woods.

One cold winter the snow was so deep
that they could not find much food.

At last a dog called to one of the foxes.

"Brother," he said, "why don't you go
and look for food? Your hair is long,
and it will keep you from getting cold.

If I go, I'll get very cold because
my hair is short."

"We foxes are all very hungry, too,"
answered the fox. "But we don't want
to go out and look for food.

, Our hair may be long, but it won't
keep us from getting cold. Let's wait
until tomorrow to look for food."

"No! Tomorrow will be too late,"
said the dog. "I want to eat today, and
I think I know how to get some food.

Far in the woods there is a fine house.
Man lives there, and he may help us.
He has lots of food, and he always has
a hot fire in his chimney.

He may help us if we dogs and foxes
go there together and ask him."

Two very old foxes gave a shout.

"Oh, no," they said. "We won't go
near Man's house. We don't know
what he will do to us."

The dog shook with the cold as he answered the foxes.

"I'm going to Man's house," he said. "I'll see if he will feed me and let me sleep by his fire. If some of you want to go with me, come now."

Not one of his brother dogs or foxes would go. So the dog went by himself.

After the dog had walked a long way through the woods, he saw Man's house. He went to the window and looked in.

Man was there in the room. He sat before a hot fire eating his dinner.

Soon Man saw the big dog standing
at the window. So he went outside and
tried to scare the dog away.

But the dog would not leave.

"I am cold and hungry," he said.

"Please let me sit near your hot fire
in the chimney place.

Please give me something to eat."

"I'll feed you," said Man. "But you
must leave my house when the food
I give you is gone."

The hungry dog went inside and sat
on the brick floor. Then Man brought
some food from a big pot by the chimney.

The dog was so hungry that he began
to eat very fast. But soon he began
to eat slower and slower.

He was trying to stay by the hot fire
as long as he could.

"Is the food I gave you gone now?"
Man asked.

"No," said the dog, and he began
to eat slower than before.

In a minute or two Man asked the dog
a second time if the food was gone.

The dog answered, "No," once again.
Then he began eating slower than ever.
He was wishing that he did not have
to go out into the cold, cold snow.

For the third time Man asked the dog
if his food was all gone.

"Yes, it is gone," answered the dog.
"But I would like to stay here with you.
I'll watch over your house if you
will keep me.

When you go out to catch animals
for food, I'll show you where to find
rabbits and squirrels and birds.

For this I will ask very little pay.
All I want is a place to sleep near
the chimney and something to eat."

"Let it be as you say," said Man.
"We will live together."

That was when dogs and foxes stopped
calling each other Brother.

That was when the dog first came to be
a friend of Man. And to this very day
they live together and help each other.

Johnny Cake

An old woman, an old man, and a boy all lived together in an old, old house.

One day the woman took some corn and made a nice, round cake for dinner.

She put the cake into a pot that was standing on the floor near the chimney. Then she told the boy to sit on the floor and watch the cake until it baked.

"Don't let it get too hot and burn," she said.

The man and the woman went to work in their garden. And the boy sat down on the floor to watch Johnny Cake.

The boy turned his head away from
the chimney to look out the window.

Then the top of the little pot flew off.

Bang! Out jumped Johnny Cake.

Across the floor and out the front door
he rolled as quick as could be.

Across the floor and out the door
ran the boy right after him.

"Stop, Johnny Cake!" cried the boy.

The old woman and the man stopped
their work and ran, too. But they were
too slow to catch Johnny Cake.

They ran and ran until they were tired.
Then they all went back home.

Johnny Cake rolled on and on and on.

"Well, well!" he thought.

"This is my kind of fun.

I roll, and they run."

Soon he rolled by a big brown bear.

"Wait just a minute!" cried the bear.
"Where are you going?"

"On and on," answered Johnny Cake.

"I have rolled away from a woman,
a man, and a boy.

I can roll away from you, too."

"Oh, you can, can you?" said the bear.
"I'll see about that."

The bear ran after Johnny Cake, but
he was not quick enough to catch him.

Next Johnny Cake saw a fox who was
sleeping in a grassy place along the road.

"Hello, there!" shouted Johnny Cake.

The fox did not move or say anything.

Johnny Cake thought the sleepy fox
had not heard him call. So he rolled
near the fox and shouted a second time.

"I have rolled away from a woman,
a man, a boy, and a bear.

I can roll away from you, too!"

The fox opened one eye and peeped
at Johnny Cake. Then he said, "Come!
Come near me and say that again.

Be quick about it!"

Johnny Cake did not know any better
than to do just what the fox told him.
He rolled up to the sleepy fox's nose
and shouted at him.

For the third time Johnny Cake said,
"I have rolled away from a boy, a man,
a woman, and a bear!

I can roll away from you, too!"

"Oh, you can, can you?" said the fox.

Then as quick as could be, he jumped
at Johnny Cake.

As quick as quick could be,
that old fox ate him up. And that
was the last of Johnny Cake.

The Wonderful Porridge Pot

Once a little girl and her mother had
nothing to eat but porridge. But they
always had all they wanted because they
owned a very wonderful porridge pot.

When they were hungry, they just put
the pot on the fire and told it to boil.

When they said, "Little Pot, boil,"
the pot started to boil at once.

They would let it boil and boil until
it was full of good hot porridge.

Then they would say, "Little Pot, stop!"

At that very minute the pot would
stop boiling.

Nearby there lived a man who had
a fine, large house and lots of money.
But the man never was happy because
the more he had, the more he wanted.

One morning he heard the woman say,
"Little Pot, boil!"

He walked across to her wee house
and looked through the window.

He saw the little black pot boiling
in the chimney. He saw it boil until
it was full of porridge.

"I must have that wonderful little pot
for my own," the man said to himself.

"I'll wait until my neighbors go away.
Then I will take the pot."

So he went home to watch and wait.

Before long the woman and the girl
came out together. Then they went off
to get sticks and straw for their fire.

After the woman and the girl had gone,
the man hurried into their house.

He ran to the big brick chimney and
picked up the porridge pot.

He took it home and put it on his fire.

"Little Pot, boil!" he said, and it
began to boil at once.

Soon the pot was full of hot porridge,
but it went right on boiling.

Hot porridge boiled out over the top
of the little pot. Porridge ran down
on the fire and down onto the floor.

255

The man ran to his chimney and took the pot off the fire. But the little pot would not stop boiling.

It boiled, and it boiled, and it boiled.

Hot porridge was running everywhere.

Over the floor, out the door, and into the street!

"This is far too much porridge for me," cried the man. "Someone must come and make the pot stop boiling."

He ran to the window and shouted, "Help, help! Quick, quick!"

The girl and her mother were coming home when they heard the call for help.

They saw hot porridge in the street, and they saw hot porridge coming out of the man's house.

They ran to the door and looked inside.

There was their own little porridge pot boiling and boiling and boiling!

"Little Pot, stop!" cried the woman.

Then the pot stopped boiling.

The man picked up the little pot and handed it to the woman.

"Take it!" he cried. "I never want to see any more porridge."

But he did see porridge for many days.

He saw it all over his floors.

He saw it all over the street.

And when he went away from home, he had to dig his way through porridge.

City Mouse and Country Mouse

One day a city mouse went to visit a friend who lived in the country.

The country mouse lived by herself under a tree. She had nothing but seeds and plants to eat. So that was what she gave her friend.

The city mouse did not care for seeds and plants. On the third day of her visit she said, "How silly you are to live here and eat this kind of food.

If you will move to the city, we will live together in a fine house. We will eat nothing but cakes, cookies, and pies."

"Oh," said her friend, "let's go now!"

So after dark the little country mouse
went home with the city mouse.

Late that night the two friends came
to the house where the city mouse lived.

They ran under the house and went up
through a hole in the floor.

Then the country mouse was in a room
that was full of good smells. They were
new smells that she knew nothing about!

Sniff, sniff, sniff went her wee nose.

Wiggle, wiggle went her tail as she
ran across the floor. And soon she was
eating good cakes and apple pie.

"Oh," she said to herself, "how silly
I was to live in the country!

I'll never go back there to live."

All at once the little city mouse saw
two big round eyes looking at her.

"Run!" she cried. "Be quick!

Here is the cat!"

With one quick jump she went through
the hole in the floor. Right after her
jumped her scared little friend.

"Well, well!" laughed the city mouse.
"We got away from the cat that time."

"Yes!" cried the little country mouse.
"But see what the cat did to my tail.

Oh, my tail! My beautiful tail!

The cat got some of my beautiful tail."

Then the city mouse laughed and said,
"If you live in the city, you must
keep watching for cats. You must
be quick, or a cat will eat you."

"Oh!" said the scared country mouse.
"I never want to live here!

You have better food here in the city
than I get in the country. But fine food
is not everything.

It is much better to live a long time
in the country than to live a short time
in the city. Good-by, my friend!"

Back to the country went the mouse,
and there she lived ever after.

The Silly Little Rabbit

Once there was a silly little rabbit who always was afraid. She was afraid that the earth would fall in.

Every time she heard a new noise, she was more afraid than ever.

One day when the wind was blowing, something fell and shook the ground.

The silly little rabbit cried, "Oh, my! The earth is falling in!

What can I do? What can I do?

I'm so afraid! I'm so afraid!"

Then that silly rabbit began running through the woods, crying to herself.

The silly rabbit met a second rabbit.

"Run, run, Brother Rabbit!" she cried.
"The earth is falling in!"

Then off she went, crying as she ran,
"I'm so afraid! I'm so afraid!"

"Oh, dear!" cried the second rabbit.
"The earth is falling in!
The earth is falling in!"

He hurried off and told another rabbit.
The third rabbit told another rabbit, and
that rabbit told another.

Soon all the rabbits in the big woods
were crying and shouting together,
"The earth is falling in!
The earth is falling in!"

The birds heard the rabbits, and they were afraid. They flew near and far, crying as they went,

"The earth is falling in!
The earth is falling in!"

The foxes and the other animals heard the birds crying, and they were afraid.

All together they began to shout,

"The earth is falling in!
The earth is falling in!
The earth is falling in!"

Soon the noise waked an old lion who
was sleeping in the big woods. He saw
foxes, bears, and rabbits running, and
he heard what they were shouting.

"Well!" said the old lion to himself.

"I must ask why all those animals
think the earth is falling in."

First the lion asked a fox about it.

"Brother Fox, who told you the earth
is falling in?" asked the lion.

"Oh, I heard it from all the birds,"
answered Brother Fox.

The birds all said, "We heard about it
from the rabbits. But we don't know
who told them."

Then one scared little rabbit looked
at the silly little rabbit and said,
"She is the one who told us."

The old lion turned to her and asked,
"Did you say the earth is falling in?"

"Yes," answered the silly little rabbit.

"How do you know?" asked the lion.

"Oh, I heard it fall, Brother Lion,"
answered the rabbit.

"Come!" said the lion. "Let's go
to the place where you heard it."

But when they got there, all they saw
was a large brown nut on the ground.

"It was just a nut that you heard fall,"
said the lion.

"Oh, my!" cried the silly little rabbit.
"Then the earth is not falling in!"

"No!" shouted the lion. "And now you
must go and tell all the other animals."

The silly little rabbit did just what the old lion told her to do.

She ran through the woods crying,

"The earth is not falling in!

The earth is not falling in!"

All the animals heard her, and they began to cry,

"The earth is not falling in!"

Back they all went to their homes.

Back they went, crying as they ran,

"The earth is not falling in!

The earth is not falling in!

The earth is not falling in!"

TO THE TEACHER

The new *Friends and Neighbors*, Book 2[1], with its accompanying *Guidebook* and *Think-and-Do Book*, continues The New Basic Reading Program for the primary grades. It is designed for approximately one semester's use whenever the child has successfully completed the new *Our New Friends*.

The new *Friends and Neighbors* has a total vocabulary of 564 words. Of these, 229 words are new in this book; 177 were introduced in Book 1[2]; 100 were new in the Primer; and the remaining 58 were introduced in the Pre-Primers.

No new words are introduced in the first unit of the book, and thereafter no page introduces more than two of the 229 new words. The first five uses of each of the 229 new words are bunched for easy mastery; there is no gap of more than five pages between any two of these first five uses. Thereafter, at spaced intervals, at least five more uses of each word occur. Each of the 334 words that were introduced in preceding books of The New Basic Reading Program is also used a minimum of ten times in the new *Friends and Neighbors*.

The 229 new words in this book are listed below. The following forms of known words are not counted as new: forms made by adding or dropping the inflectional endings *s, d, ed,* and *ing;* possessives; compounds made up of two known words. Homographs are not counted as separate words; for example, if *second* meaning "another" or "next after the first" has been introduced, *second* meaning "1/60 of a minute" is not counted as a separate word. Syllables and letters that represent sounds are not counted as new.

The red asterisks indicate 92 words that children can attack independently by applying the word-attack skills developed in The New Basic Reading Program. The type of analysis that children can use in unlocking each attack word is indicated in the *Guidebook* for the new *Friends and Neighbors*.

VOCABULARY LIST

UNIT I	12	21	30 .....
	13	22	
5	14	23	UNIT II
6	15	24	
7	16	25	31 neighbors
8	17	26	32 Pleasant
9	18	27	train *
10	19	28	33 got *
11	20	29	34 .....

268

269

159 circus
drum
160 .....
161 blew *
tired
162 winter
garden
163 parade
elephant
164 place
165 pick *
166 start *
minute
167 cut *
168 .....
169 .....
170 Goose
bake *
171 herself
clean
172 sit *
173 .....
174 late *
175 .....
176 .....

UNIT V

177 .....
178 Zeke
Tommy *
179 build
stick *
180 hand *
pile
181 himself
care

182 .....
183 shovel
digging *
184 afraid
would *
185 .....
186 potatoes
burn
187 fall *
188 watch
189 bricks *
fire
190 gave
191 .....
192 told *
won't *
193 .....
194 second
195 Miss *
sorry
196 .....
197 cold *
window
198 deep *
199 always
200 .....
201 .....
202 Christmas
203 lights *
strings
204 hurried *
205 brought *
beautiful
206 right *
207 .....
208 .....

209 spring
seeds *
210 plant *
blow *
211 those *
212 scare
213 .....
214 shook *
I'm
215 move
216 near *
217 .....
218 .....
219 .....
220 keep *
221 .....
222 .....
223 answered
224 .....
225 .....
226 turn *
227 .....
228 .....
229 .....
230 .....

UNIT VI

231 .....
232 cry *
233 Brother *
cried *
234 fox
235 .....
236 hair
237 together
chimney

238 straw
third *
239 .....
240 .....
241 .....
242 foxes
243 hot *
244 .....
245 floor *
pot *
246 .....
247 .....
248 Johnny *
Cake *
249 rolled
quick
250 .....
251 .....
252 .....
253 porridge
boil
254 .....
255 .....
256 .....
257 .....
258 country
silly *
259 .....
260 .....
261 .....
262 earth
263 .....
264 .....
265 lion
266 .....
267 .....

ACKNOWLEDGMENTS

For permission to adapt and use copyrighted material, grateful acknowledgment is made to the authors and *Children's Activities* for "I Think I Will" from "Cuthbert's Cupcakes" by Frances W. Alberts, for "Catching Tails" from "Chasing Tails" by Nancy K. Hosking, and for "A Wonderful Name" from "How Baby Cottontail Got His Name" by Flossie Winemiller; to the authors and *Child Life* for "Black Tim" from "Peter Plays Pop" by Jane Adams Parker, for "The Circus Parade" from "Tiny Elephant" by Beatrice H. Oxley, and for "Little Bear's Wish" from "The Longest Day in the Year" by Helen A. Monsell; to Thomas Nelson & Sons for "Bunny Rabbit's Home" from "Busy Bunny's New Home" in *Cuddly Kitty and Busy Bunny* by Clara G. Dennis, and for "Zeke Makes Gardens" from "The Gardeners" in *Happily Ever After* by Catherine Beebe; to Charles E. Graham & Company for "A Pie for Billy Goat" from "Piggy-Wig's Apple Pie" by Lorena Baker, and for "The Candy Tree" from "The Gum-Drop Tree" by Alice C. Dunn, both in *Little Folks* magazine; to Miriam Clark Potter and *American Childhood* for "Mrs. Goose Has a Party" adapted from "Mrs. Goose's Party"; to the authors and *The Christian Science Monitor* for "Little Rooster and the Sun" from "Who Waked the Sun?" by Letta Faunce, for "Tommy's Spring Work" from "Grape Arbor House" and for "Who Cleaned the Walk?" from "The Snowball Doorway," both by Anne Halladay; to David C. Cook Publishing Company and *Dew Drops* for "A New Game" from "Big Chief Yahoo" by Elsie Grant Henson, for "A Funny Telephone" from "Clothesline Thrills" by Ruth Bishop Juline, and for "Billy Calf Runs Away" from "The Calf Who Wanted to Travel" by Daphne Alloway McVicker; to the authors and the publishers for "The Good-by Party" from "Penny-Worth Helps with a Party" by Eleanor Hammond in *Picture Story Paper*, for "Long-Tail" from "Ginger's Strange New Baby" by Ruth Elizabeth Tanner (Copyright 1949. From *Pictures and Stories.* Used by permission.), for "Who Is Calling" from "The Barnyard Mystery" (Copyright 1950. From *Pictures and Stories.* Used by permission.), and for "Zeke and His Saw" from "Frank the Builder and His Saw" by James S. Tippett (Copyright 1950. From *Pictures and Stories.* Used by permission.); to The Judson Press for "I Won't Forget" from *The Story Shop* by Mary C. Odell; to Alice Dalgliesh for "New Friends" from "The Red Balloon" in *Junior Home Magazine*; to the author and Rand, McNally & Company for "Mrs. Hill's Birthday" from "Mrs. Mallaby's Birthday" by Helen Earle Gilbert; to G. P. Putnam's Sons for "Who Can Fool a Goat" adapted from Chapter Five of *Araminta's Goat* by Eva Knox Evans; to the author, *Storytime*, and The Baptist Sunday School Board for "The Big Surprise" from

"Wilbur and the Leaves" by Grayce Krogh; to William S. Sloan for "The Big Shovel" from "The Story of the Road Builders" by Eleanor Verdery Sloan in *American Childhood;* to Mabel Lauer Johnston for "The Biggest Apple" from "The Largest Apple in the Basket"; to the authors and *Jack and Jill* for "What Will You Buy" from "Something for Susie and Skipper" by Ida Tyson Wagner, and for "Here, There, Anywhere" from "How Ephum Played Train" by Elizabeth D. S. Stewart; to William R. Scott, Inc. for "Here Comes Father" from "Here Comes Daddy"; to Lillian F. Clark for "Bobby's New Friends" from "Freddie Finds Friends"; to Associated Publishers Inc. for "Fooling the Cats" from "The Cats and the Fowls" and for "How Man Made a Friend" from "How the Dog Became the Friend of Man," both in *African Myths* by Carter G. Woodson.

"Finding a Pet": adapted by permission from *Big, Little, Smaller and Least* by Mabel Betsy Hill. Copyright, 1936, by Frederick A. Stokes Company.

ILLUSTRATIONS

The pictures in this book were made by Keith Ward, Ellen Segner, Walter Ohlson, Marilou Wise, Connie Moran, Helen Carter, Matilda Breuer, Lillian Wuerfel, and Barbara Fitzgerald.

15 16 17 18 19 20 21 22 23 24 25   66 65 64 63 62 61